"I hate you, Miles," Diana said fiercely.

"Some people would say I was a model ex-husband," he countered. Diana gasped. His smile grew.

"Generous," he went on. "Unobtrusive. Tolerant."

"Tolerant? You?"

"Not a word of reproach about the way you've been running around the last two years," Miles said, his voice hardening. "You've made a good job of turning yourself into a rich man's houseguest, haven't you, my pet?"

Born in London, **Sophie Weston** is a traveler by nature who started writing when she was five. She wrote her first romance novel while recovering from illness, thinking her traveling days were over. She was wrong, but she enjoyed it so much that she has carried on. These days she lives in the heart of the city with two demanding cats and a cherry tree—and travels the world looking for settings for her stories.

Books by Sophie Weston

HARLEQUIN ROMANCE
3262—NO PROVOCATION
3274—HABIT OF COMMAND

Don't miss any of our special offers. Write to us at the following address for information on our newest releases.

Harlequin Reader Service
U.S.: 3010 Walden Ave., P.O. Box 1325, Buffalo, NY 14269
Canadian: P.O. Box 609, Fort Erie, Ont. L2A 5X3

Deceptive Passion
Sophie Weston

Harlequin Books

TORONTO • NEW YORK • LONDON
AMSTERDAM • PARIS • SYDNEY • HAMBURG
STOCKHOLM • ATHENS • TOKYO • MILAN
MADRID • WARSAW • BUDAPEST • AUCKLAND

ISBN 0-373-17293-1

DECEPTIVE PASSION

First North American Publication 1996.

CHAPTER ONE

DIANA put her case down with a sigh. Athens airport at six o'clock in the morning contrived to be both bleak and busy. Everyone but herself seemed to have someone to meet them.

Two years ago, she thought wryly, she would have been full of trepidation, arriving on her own. She would have been worried about finding the hired car and more than worried about driving in a foreign country to a destination she had never visited before. But that was two years ago. These days she could handle it all.

She rapped sharply on the counter of the hire car kiosk to attract attention.

'Yes?' said a bored clerk, emerging reluctantly.

'Good morning,' said Diana pleasantly. You didn't, she had learned in these years on her own, go to war at once. It was something she had picked up from watching Max. 'I believe you have a car for me.'

'We're not open yet,' the clerk said, not listening.

She stood a little straighter and said firmly, 'A car to be ready on the arrival of the six o'clock plane from Hamburg. My name is Tabard. Mrs Tabard.'

The clerk just managed not to shrug.

'We open at eight.' He turned away.

'Booked,' Diana said softly, having also learned from Max that quietness was more intimidating than the most determined ranting, 'by Count Galatas.'

The clerk stopped dead. She saw with satisfaction that his shoulders twitched as if he'd taken an arrow between them. He turned back. She smiled at him.

'Ah, yes,' he said. 'I have a note from the Count's office.'

He disappeared briefly from view and reappeared with a set of car keys and a clipboard. He needed Mrs Tabard's signature, her passport, her driving licence and that was all. He shuffled the papers dextrously.

Diana got out her American Express card only to find it waved away.

'The car is to be charged to the Count's account with our head office,' the clerk said.

He gave her an assessing look which Diana noted with some amusement. He wouldn't be used to visitors of the wealthy Galatas family arriving on tourist flights, she guessed. He was too well trained for it to show, however.

'The car is a grey Citroën. It is in the car park. The Countess left a note——' he consulted his papers '—which is in the glove compartment.'

Diana stiffened. She had not expected a personal welcome. Still less had she expected a note from the Count's erratic sister. Susie Galatas was temperamental and unpredictable but she had shown a pretty consistent desire to avoid Diana in the past. Understandable in the circumstances, of course, Diana thought wryly, since Susie had never stopped wanting Miles Tabard.

The clerk didn't appear to notice. He handed her papers back along with a keyring and a slip of paper with the registration number on it. 'The oil, water and tyres have been checked and the petrol tank is full. We ask that you return it in the same condition.' He gave her a sudden flashing smile. 'Have a wonderful holiday, Mrs Tabard. Welcome to Greece.'

'Thank you,' murmured Diana, taken aback.

She blinked. The magic of the name of the great, she thought, was something that she would never have believed without the experience of these last two years. She didn't really approve but there were times when it was useful. Times like now when she had come straight from a decaying eighteenth-century palace where she had worked non-stop through four strenuous, dusty days. A holiday would indeed be welcome.

Not that she was likely to get one in Castle Galatas. The Count's secretary had been very clear: since they were old acquaintances, the Count would be grateful if Mrs Tabard would give him a preliminary estimate for some proposed renovations. Since they were old acquaintances, he hoped she would also be able to enjoy the hospitality of the castle for a few days' break as well. Which meant, as Diana well knew, that he expected the bill to reflect that old acquaintanceship. No matter that he and his sister had disapproved of her marriage to their childhood friend and had never taken much trouble to hide their coolness.

So she gave him a slightly rueful smile which made the clerk blink in his turn. He found himself summoning a porter to take Mrs Tabard's single suitcase and guide her to the rental car.

'That one,' he said to his colleague when they were out of sight, 'will give Susanna Galatas a run for her money if anyone can.'

The girl who had just joined him looked after Diana Tabard's trim figure critically.

'But the Countess is very beautiful,' she observed. 'And rich. And she has wonderful clothes.'

'But that one,' said her mentor wisely, 'has eyes a man could drown in.'

If Diana had heard him—or understood him—she would have been astonished. She thought of herself as very ordinary. Even these days when she knew she was more elegantly turned out than she used to be. It had been a matter of pride not to fall apart when Miles left.

So she had spent a lot of time and as much money as she safely could on her appearance. On the whole she was pleased with the result. But she would never have believed that anyone thought her a worthy rival to the glamorous Countess Galatas.

She tipped the porter and slid in behind the wheel of the car. It was new and spotless. Another tribute to the status of the brother and sister Galatas, thought Diana. She had driven enough hired cars these last two years to know that they normally showed the signs of a tough existence. This one, however, started smoothly at the first turn of the key and the engine was a whisper.

Diana grinned as she went up through the tight new gears. Normally the gears were soapy and the engine chugged. If she had needed any proof of the power of the Galatas family name here it was. She hoped, she thought suddenly, that she was never on the wrong side of it.

She hoped she was doing the right thing by coming here at all. She gave an odd, superstitious shiver. Only one way to find out!

She let out the clutch on a long breath and moved gently forward into the dangerous future.

The note in the glove compartment had proved to be a map. Susie had drawn it herself evidently. Diana turned it round several times and couldn't make head or tail of it. Perhaps the Countess had decided that the best way to avoid her brother's unwanted guest was to get her lost in southern Greece, Diana thought wryly. That would be very like her in Diana's experience. Miles, of course, would never hear a word against her.

Diana had cast the map aside and hoped devoutly that she knew where she was going as well as she thought she did.

Soon enough she got used to the car and found the large, clearly signposted road to Corinth. Ignoring Susie's instructions, Diana drove steadily south. Her eyes concentrated on the road. Her tired mind wandered.

She had never come to the castle with Miles. They had meant to; even planned to that last year. But with the coming of autumn, when the schedule in the kitchen said, 'Chris and Susie: Greece', she and Miles were in different continents. By that time they were no longer communicating except through solicitors. No longer, thought Diana painfully, even trying to pretend they had a marriage.

The sun was getting high. She extracted sunglasses one-handed from her bag and pushed them up her small nose. The glare of the metalled road was blinding. She nearly missed the turning off the main highway. She braked sharply and swung off on to the side road she remembered from poring over the Greek road maps Miles had left behind. Soon she was passing as many mule-drawn carts as lorries.

Miles, she remembered, always said the road to the Galatas castle was the last prehistoric route in Europe. So it must get tougher than this. Diana's mouth thinned. Miles had, nevertheless, negotiated whatever hazards the road presented without mishap from the day he got his driving licence. She wasn't going to do any less.

She quelled the treacherous flicker of trepidation. If Miles could do it, she could. It was the principle that had got her through the last two years.

Later, towards mid-morning, she looked at the petrol gauge. These last two years had taught her that on a road you didn't know you filled up whenever you could. She had never thought of that before. And Miles, of course, had never explained why he was putting petrol into a half-full tank. He had never explained why he was doing anything: he just did it. Silently, competently and, in the end, with a sizzling impatience that had kept Diana's nerves on the stretch for months, waiting for the final explosion.

The garage came into view. She drove into it and got out, stretching. The sun was like a physical presence at her shoulder after the greyness of Hamburg and London. She explained to the proprietor what she wanted in her few words of careful Greek and sat at a table in the shade with a coffee while her instructions were carried out by a teenage boy in overalls.

Diana closed her eyes, tilting her chair back until her head rested against the wall behind her. Miles, of course, had spoken fluent Greek. Well, he had been practically brought up by old Count Galatas after his parents split up. He and the old man's two grandchildren had more or less run wild at the castle in the school holidays from what she had gathered.

Diana took off her dark glasses. Maybe that was when Miles had got his taste for danger. She remembered one story of Miles and Chris diving off the castle battlements into the sea. The old Count had made them apologise to the fishermen who had pulled them out— and who, Diana thought, the boys must have frightened into heart attacks. And he made them chop wood as a penance. Nothing much there to deter a repeat performance, Diana had said drily.

Miles had been surprised.

'Repeat? Why should we? We'd proved we could do it. It's boring to repeat things. They become a habit. Where's the fun in a habit?'

Marriage, of course, had all too rapidly become a habit for Miles; one with no fun in it at all.

In a way, thought Diana, she'd almost expected it. The brilliance, the restlessness, the sharp sense of him always being on the edge of danger—they had all made him seem very strange and somehow intimidating. Even when they were first married and she was so in love with him that she could tell when he walked into a room with a hundred people between them, she had never felt quite at ease with him. Not as a wife should with her husband, Diana thought now.

There was a murmur at her elbow. She turned. It was the garage proprietor bearing a wooden tray with a glass of water, a smaller glass of some clear liquid and a dish of olives and little gobbets of fat bacon. He put it down and gestured, smiling.

Diana guessed what it was. She raised the glass to her lips and the smell of aniseed hit her like a blow. Ouzo.

Memory struck too, like a snake. Miles drank it every evening. A greeting to the night, he had said, laughing. Diana didn't like the taste much so she didn't usually join him. But later, when they kissed, it would still be there: the hint of aromatic heat and herbs that spoke of another country and all the foreign unguessable things in Miles's nature.

He could have been standing there with his lop-sided mocking smile. She could not have been less shocked if she had turned and found him beside her.

'This has got to stop,' Diana said to herself firmly.

She threw the spirit down her throat quickly. Her eyes filled with tears—due, she assured herself, entirely to the strength of the ouzo. She finished the water, thanked the proprietor and paid her bill.

She was not going to spend the rest of this, her first journey alone in Greece, with Miles as an invisible, mocking companion, she told herself. She had survived his departure. She was not going to fall apart now. She would put him out of her mind.

It should be a reasonably straight route from now on. Diana set off again, with determined confidence.

That confidence was hard won. She'd had none at all when she first met the Galatas family. It had been clear right from the start that any of Miles's friends who'd thought he might yet marry had had Susie Galatas picked out as the only candidate. He had been escorting her everywhere she wanted to go for fifteen years, and her brother was his best friend. And she was gorgeous. It would have been the ideal match—especially as Susie was wildly in love with him.

Or so they said. Susie herself denied it, of course. And Miles was very fond of her. Even after they were married he dropped everything whenever Susie rang, wanting to see him. It had been one of the first signs that all was not well with the marriage.

So why me in the first place? Diana bit her lip unhappily.

It always came back to that. It always had done, right from the first. She had never quite believed it. Miles was brilliant; to a modest history undergraduate he seemed utterly inaccessible.

At thirty-six, he was the youngest professor by ten years in the university. All his female students were in love with him. He wasn't classically good-looking but he had the proud, intense air of a visionary—and, it must be admitted, the body of an athlete, Diana thought wryly. They had had reason enough for their crushes, those devoted students of his.

Only she hadn't had a crush on him. She wasn't in his class and she had known him only by reputation. She had been overwhelmed with shyness when they were introduced. And after that first stammering exchange she had never expected to see him again.

Miles had decided otherwise. He chased her relent-lessly. Everyone noticed—most of them before Diana did. Even her elderly tutor had warned her uncom-fortably—and at the time inexplicably—about the dangers of relationships between sophisticated older men and innocent young girls. And she had been, thought Diana, horribly innocent.

She sighed, taking the car round a steeply sloped double bend with her new-won competence. Was it her innocence that had intrigued Miles? Had he always, in the private core of himself that he guarded from her, been secretly laughing at her naïve wonder?

Because, for Diana, Miles had been a revelation. She had not even attempted to disguise it. It had amused him, she remembered that. In fact he was usually amused; amused, sure of himself, passionate in a way that Diana had never even dreamed of. Even now she blushed if she strayed into too explicit memories of the passion between them. And in the end he had been passionate in his unrelenting hostility, too.

Diana's heart began to beat hard as she remembered those last terrible weeks. He had behaved as if she had betrayed him somehow. As if she had trapped him into marriage; as if she had set out to deceive him.

In the end she'd decided that he must suddenly have realised that the image he'd had of her when they married—whatever it was—was wrong and blamed her for it. It was the only reasonable explanation. But it still didn't answer the question which still haunted her after all these months, the beginning and the end of the whole thing: why, in the first place, why *me*?

The road forked. Without hesitation, Diana curved to the left. She had heard Miles talk about this road often enough. The steering-wheel was hot. Beyond the purring engine there was the heavy silence of the Mediterranean noon. Diana leaned forward.

Slowly, as the car breasted the hill, the sea came into sight—a glimmer of silver between two heat-hazed hills ahead. The road became stones and then sand. It climbed and dipped and the sea, glimpsed between outcrops of rock, came closer. It was the colour of ink at the horizon, paling to silver at the edge of the rocks where it furled along the shore below. In the distance she could hear the rise and fall of the tide against the rocks.

Diana sighed. Absolute peace, just as the Count's secretary had promised. No wonder Miles had loved it.

She stopped the thought abruptly. Miles again. She would *not* be invaded like this. She set her mouth angrily. She was never going to see him again and she had to get used to it.

The last she heard he was on the other side of the world, lecturing in Sydney. And for the next fortnight at least she was going to be here in Greece on a working holiday, to all intents and purposes alone. There would be the servants, of course. But Christos Galatas, or rather his shrewd secretary, had negotiated an undisturbed holiday as part of the package.

It was odd, thought Diana, how she could organise a solitary professional and social life without difficulty but was reduced to despair by the prospect of holidaying alone. Maybe she wasn't as strong as she thought yet.

But she would be, she promised herself. After all she had a life to live. She would have to shake off Miles's overwhelming shadow and find more than work to fill her days. He had.

Miles's friends seemed to expect him to marry Susie as soon as he and Diana divorced—as he probably should have done years ago. Her eyes felt gritty. The car jolted as it turned a particularly savage corner. Diana swore and then stopped, silenced by the vista before her.

It was the castle: a grim Venetian fortress, dark to the point of unreality against the splendid glow of sea and sky. Diana drew a long, appreciative breath.

Beautiful, yes, and with a near-vertical approach road. Diana laughed softly. Two years ago she wouldn't have contemplated driving up that suicidal road. At least Miles's defection had taught her to do things she was afraid of. Carefully she put the car into second gear and gunned the accelerator.

It went up the incline like a slightly unsteady bullet and came to rest—just—under an olive tree in the deeply shadowed courtyard. Miles's childhood home. There was no one about.

Diana crossed her arms on the steering-wheel and leaned her forehead against them. For no reason at all she felt like crying.

A woman came out of a small arched doorway. Diana sat up at once, confused. But it wasn't Susie, cool and polished, in one of her Paris outfits. It was a short square woman with greying dark hair and heavy brows.

'Mrs Tabard?' she asked in a heavy accent.

Diana got swiftly out of the car.

'Yes. I made good time.' She looked up at the forbidding walls.

The woman smiled and gestured to herself. 'Maria.'

She spoke at length. Diana's Greek gave out after the greetings. It was possible that Maria wanted her to have a meal.

'All I want,' Diana said slowly and with feeling, 'is a rest.'

Maria stared. A little desperately, Diana put her hands together and rested her cheek against them, making snoring noises. Maria's face broke into a beam of delighted comprehension.

'*Hypno,*' she said, as far as Diana could make out.

There was no misunderstanding the imperative wave with which she gestured to Diana to follow her, however. She seized the overnight bag from the passenger seat and set off across the courtyard into the cool darkness of stone walls and winding stairs.

Diana was soon lost. Eventually they came to a wide corridor with windows on one side and heavy unpolished wooden doors on the other. Maria flung back one of them.

'Bed,' she said proudly.

Over her shoulder Diana had a brief impression of a tall room with a profusion of floor-to-ceiling Venetian mirrors. She also detected a four-poster, a *petit point* Louis-Quatorze chair and a monstrous Victorian dressing-table. Diana blinked.

Maria, she saw, was unimpressed by this costly jumble. She closed the door smartly and took her to the next door in the corridor. She opened it with a flourish. This was clearly the more impressive room in Maria's estimation.

'Bath.'

It was indeed. It was a room of immense proportions, fully as big as the bedroom next door, with a brass Edwardian shower stall at one end and a bath as big as a boat on huge brass claw feet in the middle of the floor. In an attempt to reduce the air of vastness, presumably, someone had surrounded it with a profusion of tables, chairs and mirrors. There was even a quilted bathrobe hanging on the door that led to the bedroom, presumably for passing guests.

Diana swallowed. Since she had entered her new profession she had become something of an expert in period bathrooms, and this was unique in her experience.

'Bath,' repeated Maria, a little impatiently.

'So I see,' Diana agreed faintly. 'I mean, thank you.'

Putting down Diana's overnight bag on a gilt chair, Maria swung energetically at a heavy brass lever sprouting from the edge of the bath. Water gushed from the central tap. It looked, thought Diana, like one of the water spouts from Notre Dame. Steam rose.

'Hot,' said Maria unnecessarily.

She adjusted the temperature with a number of expert tweaks. Then, under Diana's bemused eyes, she took a flagon the size of a stage prop from one of the glass-topped tables and swirled a liberal amount of oil into the water. A smell of white lilac infused the steam. Maria turned off the tap. Then, pointing to a pile of fluffy towels on a tapestry chair, she left.

Diana began to laugh. Maria was almost certainly right. She was hot and stiff and dusty. The scented water looked wonderful. Her long-delayed sleep could wait another ten minutes.

She stripped off her cotton jeans and shirt and let them fall to the floor. Her underwear was silk, beautifully cut and expensive, severely bare of the lace or bows she had favoured in the days when she had bought it as much for Miles's pleasure as her own. Not, she thought ruefully, that he had ever shown any signs of noticing. All he had ever wanted was to rid her of the delicate garments as swiftly as possible.

'*Stop* thinking about him,' she said aloud, sitting down in the middle of the 'boat' with a distinct splash.

She soaked for as long as she dared. It would be all too easy to fall asleep, she knew. She rotated her shoulders under the scented water, feeling the stiffness dissolve. A not unpleasant sense of unreality began to invade her. She got out at last, dreamily, wrapped herself in one of the large towels and padded through the connecting door into the bedroom she had been shown.

The shuttered darkness was cool. Diana drifted pleasurably to the curtained bed—and stopped dead. All her sense of well-being dropped from her abruptly.

For there was someone lying under the woven coverlet, one bare brown shoulder visible. He was face-down, a tanned arm flung up on the pillow round his sleeping head. The muscles were impressive and the tan the colour of fresh toast. He looked like a resting runner. He stirred, murmuring.

Diana's mouth went dry. Her hands closed convulsively on the knot she had made of the towel at her breasts. She took a step backwards.

He turned his face on the pillow. She could see the arrogant profile, the steep lids and the incongruous curl of hair that flicked round under his ear no matter what he did. Not that she needed to. She had already recognised those muscles. The shadows muted the Venetian red to chestnut but Diana knew the colour of his hair as well as she knew her own.

His lashes lifted gently and dropped at once. He was still unconscious, it seemed.

Diana pulled herself together. Carefully, putting one foot silently behind the other, she retreated, never taking her eyes off the bed.

It was the mirror that spoilt it. She had forgotten it was there and, catching sight of her own reflection's movement out of the corner of her eye, she gave an involuntary gasp.

It was enough. He had always, she thought bitterly, been a light sleeper.

He came awake, as he had always done, instantly. Diana froze. He turned his head.

There was a long, agonising silence. Her hands clenched so tight on her towel that the luxurious stuff marked her.

Very slowly he lifted himself on to his elbow. He surveyed her thoroughly. The key pattern coverlet fell away, revealing that his tan extended to his hips. Diana's thoughts scurried like rabbits let out of a cage. Only one clear message came through and that was one she didn't want: that he must have been working in the open for weeks to get so evenly brown.

Their eyes met. He gave a slow, sleepy smile. Diana felt something cold run up and down her spine and lodge solidly in the pit of her stomach.

'Unexpected,' Miles said huskily.

Her whole body was shaking with tension. He mustn't see it, she thought frantically. She knew she should move—turn her back on him and return to the sanctuary of the bathroom and her discarded clothes. Where was the strength of will she had spent the last two years nurturing? Hadn't she been congratulating herself on it only this morning?

But Diana could only stand and tremble. She felt that sensual regard envelop her like a warm breeze and despised herself.

With a suddenness that made her jump, he flung aside the coverlet and held out his hand. It was quite explicit. For a moment something inside her flared up in response to that wicked invitation.

Diana flinched. She was appalled. She shook her head vigorously. It must be because she was so tired—or the shock of finding him here—or the ouzo on the sunny road——

'God, *no*,' she said in a rag of a voice.

It seemed her hard-won poise had gone along with her strength of will. She bit her lip, struggling for composure, some semblance of dignity. He watched her, one eyebrow raised. He looked, she thought, amused. It was not surprising, or even out of character, but it made her feel ashamed.

'Why——?' he began softly.

But she interrupted him. 'I'm sorry,' she said. 'There's been a misunderstanding. I've only just arrived. No one was about except Maria, and I suppose she didn't understand.'

It came out high and breathless but at least she wasn't gibbering, Diana thought drily. Or asking what in the world he was doing here when he ought to be the other side of the world. Or screaming at him.

'It was probably my fault,' she went on, trying to sound composed. 'I've been travelling a long time and I'm tired. I must have got the wrong end of the stick. I'm sorry if I've disturbed you.'

His look of amusement deepened. He leaned back against the pillows, his hands clasped behind his head.

'You've done that all right.'

Diana blushed. She could feel the colour flooding into her face. Miles had always been able to make her blush, just by looking at her.

He watched with interest. She could—if she had been close enough and not shaking with reaction—have hit him.

'I'm sorry,' she said again coldly. 'There'll be a room for me somewhere. I'll go and——'

It was his turn to interrupt. 'Why bother? There's plenty of room here.'

It was, indeed, the biggest bed she'd ever seen in her life. Even with his six-foot frame stretched across it, there was space for several additional bodies. There was not, however, room enough for her.

'I wouldn't dream . . .'

'Why?' he said again very softly. He met her eyes, his own rueful. 'You're worn out. You said so. Maria goes to ground in the afternoon. God knows how you found her in the first place. She'll have evaporated by now. Why not give up and crash out till evening?'

Diana glared at him. 'Because you're here.'

'But not in exclusive possession.' His voice was bland. 'I've offered to share.'

Diana drew a long breath. 'I don't think that would be a good idea,' she said with a calm she was proud of.

There was a gleam in the brown eyes. 'Unrestful, you think? Well, there are remedies for that.' His voice was blatantly teasing.

Diana stopped even trying to play his game.

'You must think I'm an awful fool,' she said with heat. 'It would take nothing short of anaesthesia to get me into that bed with you.'

His lids dropped. He was laughing.

'I'll bear that in mind.'

There was no answer to that. Diana shrugged unwarily and caught at her towel just in time. Her blush redoubling, she turned away. She was conscious of his eyes on her shoulders above the bath-towel. How could eyes suggest so much? she thought in irritation.

He said idly, 'Where are you going to sleep? In the bath?'

'If I have to.' Her voice was grim. 'But I'll have a go at finding Maria first.'

'It might be easier to find Susie.'

His voice was mild enough, almost idle. But Diana knew him well indeed and she recognised a challenge when she heard one. She whipped round.

'Susie?' She was frankly appalled. It had never occurred to her that her undisturbed holiday would include a hostess who despised her. 'She's *here*?'

His mouth tilted wryly. 'It's her home.'

'But she hardly ever came...' Diana said, and stopped dead on a shaft of memory.

It had been Christos, at a long-ago party, taking the wind out of Susie's sails. She'd been clinging to Miles's arm, reminding him of the wonderfully simple life at the castle—a life of course which Diana had never shared. Diana had been rather grateful for Chris's intervention.

'You don't like the simple life, Susie,' he had said dampeningly. 'No nightclubs, no shops, no friends to party with. You never go to the castle any more.'

And Susie had looked adoringly up at Miles and said softly, 'Neither does Miles.'

She hadn't said she'd live in a desert if Miles were there. She hadn't had to. And here he was.

Diana stared at him. They must be here together. Her mind worked frantically. The perfect secretary must be less than perfect after all. She couldn't have known. Unless...

She said carefully, 'Did you know I was coming?'

The lop-sided grin grew. 'Of course,' he said with composure.

Her hands clenched tight into fists. He noted it, she saw. His brows rose.

'I let Maria think that Susie had gone out and wouldn't be back till after you got here. Whenever that was.' He added thoughtfully, 'I didn't really think it'd be till this evening. It was very silly of you not to have a rest in Athens.'

Diana ignored that. 'You—told—Maria——'

'That when you arrived she was to bring you straight up,' he said, watching her intently.

She opened her mouth to shout at him. Then shut it again. She couldn't think of anything devastating enough to say to express her feelings.

He watched her unblinkingly. He was still completely relaxed. It was only too obvious that he found the situation highly amusing and was interested to see how she would get out of it.

'*Why*?' she said at last in a strangled voice.

'Use your imagination,' he invited softly.

This can't be happening, she thought. It *can't*. It's worse than my worst nightmares. I'll wake up in a minute and find I've crashed the car... But she met his amused, level gaze and knew it was all too real.

'You're mad,' Diana said at last. She made a helpless gesture. 'I suppose you know why you're doing this.' She hitched her towel in front of her more securely. 'Are you going to tell me where I find my own room, or would you find it more amusing if I have to play hunt the thimble up and down this damned castle?'

One eyebrow flew up. 'In your bath-towel? Now that definitely has its attractions.'

'I'm glad to entertain you, of course,' Diana said with equal courtesy and untruth, 'but I would like...'

To her horror she found her eyes filling with unexpected, traitorous tears. She flung away from him quickly.

'The hell with you. I'll find Maria,' she said in a curt voice.

He spoke from behind her. For the first time he didn't sound amused.

'Diana...'

But she fled. She knew that voice and it was the one he used when he was determined to get his own way. She had learned to resist after a fashion—but not when she was tired, on the edge of tears, and wrapped in someone else's bath-towel. The odds, Diana thought, with slightly uncertain humour, had to be evened a little before she was ready to do battle with a master.

She locked the bathroom door and scrambled into her clothes. They looked even worse than they had when she arrived, wrinkling over her slightly damp skin. Diana didn't care. She had never had the clothes to compete with Susie anyway. And this was worse than the social embarrassment of being scruffy in the presence of the elegant Countess.

She found her with Maria's help. The Greek woman looked concerned, but she took one look at Diana's set pallor and uncurled herself from her comfortable chair. She escorted her to a heavy door and knocked.

Diana heard Susie's voice. A cold hand clenched round her heart. She had hoped not to hear it again.

'Come in.'

She did.

It was a huge room, full of flowers. They were crimson and purple and white, trailing from bowl to antique bowl so that it looked like a garden. In the middle of this riot, Susie lay on a chaise-longue reading a foolscap file.

There was a faint frown between the heavy brows. She looked up impatiently. As soon as she saw Diana her expression changed. It became cool and guarded. She did, however, stand up to greet her guest. Her unwanted guest, Diana reminded herself.

'Diana. I didn't know you'd arrived.' She brushed a scented cheek half an inch from Diana's. 'Good journey?'

But Diana wasn't playing social games. She found she was shaking. She drew a deep breath and said in a voice as cool as her adversary's, 'Susie, what is Miles Tabard doing in my bed?'

CHAPTER TWO

SUSIE seemed to go rigid. Her eyes not quite meeting Diana's, she said, 'I don't know what you mean.'

Diana said, 'I thought I was supposed to be here on a working holiday. *On my own*. Nobody said it was on my own except for my ex-husband.'

Susie was cool. 'And me.'

It was only a pin-prick but it still hurt. Susie had no doubt intended it to hurt, thought Diana. Susie was telling her that Miles travelled with her these days. Diana didn't entirely believe her but she still flinched from the message.

She said equally coolly, 'It wasn't you I walked in on, though. Was it?'

The heavy brows went up. 'Walked in on?'

Diana shuddered suddenly, remembering. Those mocking, knowing eyes. That careless invitation to which she had—oh, so nearly—responded.

Susie looked disgusted. 'For heaven's sake. You lived with the man for two years. There's no need to go on as if he's Sweeney Todd.'

Diana shook her fair head. 'It isn't that. You don't understand. I really did walk in on him, Susie. In bed. Maria just showed me into the room and...'

She couldn't go on. If Miles chose to tell Susie about her appearance from the bathroom wrapped in a towel, she couldn't prevent it, she thought. And if they were as close as rumour had it then he probably would. Eventually, anyway. But Diana couldn't.

Susie's eyes flickered. She shrugged.

25

'Since I take it he was in bed alone, I don't see what the fuss is about,' she said but her voice was strained. 'You did it daily up to two years ago.'

'It was different then,' Diana said bleakly.

She was remembering. Two years ago, they had been barely speaking. Four years ago they had been in love. Whenever she walked into a room where Miles was, he would turn his head and smile at her. She remembered the physical sensation like touching electricity, whenever she met the warm brown eyes.

When he'd invited her to bed then, it hadn't been a challenge, a way of watching her squirm. It had been tender, passionate, laughing and infinitely gentle. Tears threatened again. She turned her head, furious with herself.

Susie said curtly, 'Look, I don't know why there was a mix-up about your room. I'll sort it out. I've only just arrived myself. I haven't had time to talk to Maria yet.'

Diana ignored that. She said quietly, 'All you had to do was tell me you'd be here, Susie. I wouldn't have come.'

Something flashed in the black cherry eyes. 'You'd have preferred to be alone with Miles?'

This time Diana prevented herself from shuddering.

'I'd have preferred to be alone. Full stop.'

Susie looked at her carefully. 'I believe you would.' She sounded blank.

'I assure you I would,' Diana agreed wryly.

Susie shook her head. She sank down on the chaise-longue again. The rigidity seemed to go out of her.

'I didn't know you were coming,' she said at last. 'Nobody told me. I wasn't intending to be here myself but—well, something came up and I wanted to leave Athens.' A small, unhappy smile crossed her face. 'Not the ideal holiday for either of us.'

Diana took a decision. 'I'll go.'

At once Susie's head came up. She looked alarmed.

'You mustn't do that. They'll blame me. Chris is angry enough with me as it is.' She sounded genuinely worried.

'I'm sorry,' said Diana without much truth. On the whole she tried to help people out, but her charity towards Susie Galatas had diminished in direct proportion to the attention her husband had afforded the Countess in the year before they parted.

Susie said rapidly, 'Look, I don't know what's going on but I think Chris and Miles put their heads together. They'll never forgive me if I louse it up.'

Diana stared, bemused. 'Are you saying I was deliberately brought here under false pretences?' she demanded slowly.

Susie bit her lip. 'Miles may want to see you. He hasn't said anything to me, but... Is it so impossible?' she flashed with sudden bitterness.

Diana didn't believe it. In two years Miles hadn't written or made so much as a telephone call at New Year. He had asked for a meeting in the solicitor's offices a couple of times, of course, but Diana was fairly sure that was at her solicitor's instigation. Her solicitor had taken his moral obligation to attempt a reconciliation very seriously. In the end she had had to tell him frankly that she couldn't bear seeing Miles again that way.

'But if Miles——' she stumbled over the name '—wanted to get in touch he had only——'

'To write to your solicitor. I know. He said.' Susie sighed. 'I agree with you, that would have been the most sensible. What's the point in scratching over old wounds? But Miles——' She shrugged again. 'You know what he's like. He wants his own way. I heard Miles tell Chris he asked for a meeting three times and you wouldn't agree. That,' she added unnecessarily, 'annoyed him.'

So that was why he had conspired with Chris in setting this trap. Determination not to be bested by her evasive tactics. His determination was one of the things that Diana had most loved about him. Once. She bit back sudden, infuriating tears. Tiredness, she assured herself savagely.

When she had mastered her voice she said carefully, 'We had nothing to say to each other. It could only have been—painful.'

'You mean you couldn't face it,' Susie interpreted accurately.

Diana's eyes flickered. She didn't answer. Susie sighed angrily.

'Well, he's here now. And so are you. What are you going to do about it?'

'I—don't know,' Diana said in a voice that was hardly a voice at all. 'Look, Susie, I can't talk about this now. I'm so tired I can't think straight. Can you find me somewhere—anywhere—to lie down for a couple of hours? Maybe I'll start making sense after that.'

'But Miles . . .'

'*Please*,' said Diana with the quiet firmness that had worked so signally on the car rental clerk.

It worked on Susie too. She gave a small shrug.

'If that's what you want. I thought you'd like a room in the eighteenth-century bit, overlooking the terrace.' She hesitated and then said almost angrily, 'There'll be the whole castle between you and Miles. So you don't have to worry about him creeping up on you when you're asleep.'

Diana did not answer.

The room was exquisite. Diana looked round at the creamy hangings and delicate furniture and thought wryly how different it was from the room Miles inhabited. Or Susie for that matter. They were obviously on the family corridor. She wondered, briefly and painfully, whether they visited each other's rooms.

Though there was something in the other woman's manner that told her they didn't. She seemed angry, bitter even. Not like the successful rival confronting the old love.

'Oh, it's all so *difficult*,' she said aloud.

For the second time that afternoon she stepped out of her clothes. She was already more than half asleep as she slipped between the rosemary-scented sheets.

She didn't stir when Susie looked in an hour later. She didn't stir when Maria brought up her suitcase and placed it on the folding stool beside the bathroom door. Maria chuckled maternally and let herself out with only the minimum creaking of ancient hinges. Diana never moved.

She came wide awake, though, instantly, when the door closed behind Miles.

He stood with his hands behind him against the door, watching her sardonically.

'Recovered?'

Diana hauled herself up on the pillows, clutching the covers cautiously to her chest. She was wearing her underwear, which, she thought wryly, was better than a towel but not much. She schooled her expression. So much for Susie's belief that Miles would not invade her room, she thought. For all their shared childhood and Susie's own barely disguised predilection, she sometimes wondered how well Susie Galatas really knew Miles.

'Recovering,' she said coolly. 'I've got a lot of sleep to catch up on.'

'And you want me to push off while you do,' he interpreted softly.

She inclined her head. The fair hair was straining at the pins that kept it knotted at the nape. She winced. Miles saw it.

'Take them out,' he said.

Diana flinched. The sudden memory was vivid; too vivid. The times he had sat on the edge of the bed behind her, taking out the hairpins one by one; massaging her shoulders gently; kissing the back of her neck. Her eyes slid away from him as she fought the memory down.

'What do you want, Miles?' she asked.

His eyes were still on her hair. 'Why don't you take it down, for God's sake? You know it gives you a headache if you sleep with it up like that.'

Diana tensed. But she replied calmly enough, 'Thank you for your advice. What do you *want*?'

He came right into the room then and stood at the foot of the bed. He scanned her. It was odd, thought Diana confusedly, that a man with such a mobile, expressive face could be so completely unreadable when he chose.

'A talk,' he said at last coolly. 'A few words. Nothing more.'

Miles picked up a three-legged, fan-backed chair and swung it round so he could sit astride it, looking at her. He crossed his arms along the back and dropped his chin on them.

She watched him warily. He looked, thought Diana, irritated, like a scientist confronted with an interesting specimen.

'So speak,' she said curtly, looking away.

'Susie said you weren't staying.' He sounded indifferent. Diana mistrusted him thoroughly. 'Because of me.'

Diana was startled. She had not been together enough to make a decision like that, and Susie knew it. She had even urged her to stay. What game was the Countess playing? she wondered.

Though, of course, it was really the only sensible thing to do—to leave now before it all got recriminatory and hurtful.

Diana moved restlessly. 'So?'

His eyes were very steady. 'Is it true?'

She didn't know the answer to that even now. She burst out, 'What did you expect, for heaven's sake? That I would walk into the trap and say thank you?'

The brown eyes flickered. 'Trap?'

Diana made a weary gesture. 'What else would you call it? It was obvious what you planned. Getting me to a nice remote castle where I couldn't easily get away.'

His eyes narrowed. 'So I'm scheming against you? Planning a kidnap, maybe?' he said softly.

'What else is this?' she flung at him.

He put his head on one side, considering it. His fingers drummed on the fragile back of the chair.

'Why should I do that?' he parried.

Diana shook her head. 'That's what I said. It makes no sense. But Susie told me you and Chris conspired behind my back.'

His mouth slanted in an unamused smile. 'And you and Susie have been discussing me behind my back,' he pointed out, even more softly.

Diana curbed an instinct to apologise. He had always been able to do that: put her in the wrong so she backed away from what would have been a legitimate protest.

She glared at him. 'Don't I have a right to defend myself? Who else would tell me what's going on, for God's sake?'

That, she saw with satisfaction, got him on the raw. His eyebrows flew up as if she had astonished him. For a moment he looked as taut and dangerous as she had ever seen him. Diana's muscles locked in tension.

Then, with one of those bewildering changes of mood, he was laughing. The brown eyes, astonishingly, were warm, even caressing.

'You're growing up,' he said, propping his chin on his hands again. 'What else was I to do? I couldn't get past your damned obstructive solicitor.'

'Why should you want to?' Diana demanded harshly.

Miles looked surprised. 'You're my wife. We need to talk. Surely you can see that?'

She winced. 'Why? We never talked when we were married.'

For a moment he didn't answer. Then he said gently, 'We're still married.'

She was shaken with a gust of anger. He hadn't remembered they were married when he walked out two years ago. He hadn't wanted to remember since, either.

'And that gives you the right to manipulate me? Amuse yourself a little, maybe? At my expense, of course.' She couldn't keep the bitterness out of her voice.

Miles watched her, his face unreadable. But he said lightly enough, 'There's a certain humour in the situation certainly. Though you don't seem to see it yourself. So what are you going to do? Cut and run?'

Diana sighed, the anger draining out of her. Her head was beginning to thump. Absently she started to take out the hairpins.

'I don't know,' she admitted. 'I haven't thought much beyond this fortnight for weeks. Frankly, I'm too tired to climb back into the car and make a break for freedom today.'

Miles made an involuntary movement, quickly stilled. 'Do you want me to go?' he asked her unexpectedly.

Diana jumped. For the first time she remembered he was supposed to be in Australia. Had something gone wrong?

'What are you doing here?' she asked slowly.

Miles hesitated. 'We cut the lecture schedule. Steve's gone back to England for a holiday.'

Overwork, Diana diagnosed, hearing what he wasn't saying. Neither Miles nor Steve Gilman had any sense of self-preservation when they were working. They must have driven themselves to the end of endurance. Miles would need a holiday. And this was the home of much of his childhood.

She said, 'You shouldn't have to leave. This is your place.'

Miles shrugged again. 'I've never been a permanent resident. I can come back any time and resume my own holiday.'

Diana shook her head decisively. 'Not on my account. I bet you need this break.'

His mouth twisted in a small, private smile. She had learned to fear that smile. She never knew what it meant.

'Same old Diana,' he said softly. 'I wondered. I can see I needn't have done. Waifs and strays and needy persons this way.' He stood up suddenly, swinging the chair one-handed back to its place against the wall. 'Yes, I need a break. But I'm not on my last legs. I could go and play with the tourists on one of the islands if it would make you any happier.'

'No,' said Diana swiftly, making up her mind. 'No. I'll go. Oh, maybe not today. Or even tomorrow. But when I've got my breath back.'

Miles said without expression, 'Running away, Diana?'

She closed her eyes briefly. 'Is that so surprising?'

'Running doesn't help, you know,' he said gently. 'You have to turn and face the truth one day. Why not sooner rather than later?'

She made a helpless gesture. 'Don't.'

But he pursued his advantage ruthlessly.

'It would be such very public running, too. Susie's not the only one here with us, you know. Chris is down for a few days. And——' he hesitated '—an old boyfriend of Susie's. They'll talk if you pack your bags and bolt. Are you sure you feel equal to dealing with it? I thought you always wanted to settle our differences in private.'

It was true. Diana had fought to maintain the appearance of a united front for months after Miles had stopped speaking to her except in that clipped, cold way. She had taken his arm in public; smiled at him across dinner tables; pretended she knew where he was when people rang. He had accused her then of not facing up to things. And in the end he had made her face them. When he left her.

She felt the old sense of helpless incomprehension begin to take hold. She pushed it down firmly. She wasn't helpless any more. And she understood Miles only too well.

'Our differences are pretty public now, I think,' she said quietly.

He gave a little nod, like a chess player acknowledging an opponent's move.

'True enough. But Susie at least will demand a blow-by-blow account of what we've said to each other if you leave now,' he said at last carefully. 'You won't enjoy that, you know.'

It was true. Diana gave a little shiver. He knew her too well, this man.

'What do you want me to do, then?' she muttered.

He showed no indecent triumph. He didn't laugh at her capitulation. Indeed, he seemed to be choosing his words as carefully as if she had not given in at all.

'Give it a chance. Just a few days. We can be polite to each other that long, surely?'

Diana did not even try to meet his eyes. Miles could school his features like an actor, she had learned. And his expression was no clue to his feelings.

'I suppose so,' she said reluctantly.

'You won't see much of me,' he assured her, his tone dry. 'I'm in the fields most of the day. Or out on the boat.'

She said, 'I'll try to keep out of your way, then.'

He stood up at once. She felt a little spurt of resentment. Of course he would go, once she'd agreed to do what he wanted. And she wanted him to go, didn't she? After all she didn't want to talk to him. It was illogical to mind. It was just, she assured herself, that it was all too humiliatingly familiar.

'I'll see you at dinner, then.'

She thought he was going and felt the tension drain out of her. So it was all the greater shock when he took two long strides towards her. His arm snaked out and before she knew what he was doing he had flicked the last confining pins out of her hair.

It fell in a fair, feathery cloud. Diana felt it brush her shoulders and then, rigid with disbelief, felt his fingers looping it gently aside. As if they were still married, as if he had never hurt and deserted her, Miles Tabard bent and brushed his mouth against her exposed nape.

She gave a little gasp of outrage and jerked away from him. But he was laughing. And then he was gone.

When Susie came to fetch her before dinner, Diana was seriously reconsidering her decision.

Susie was wearing a simple cotton caftan with a bold geometric pattern in red and purple. Her hair was piled on top of her head in a coronet that made her look serene and royal. She was wearing, Diana saw, what were probably thousands of pounds' worth of platinum and rubies at her ears and wrists. Her bare feet were in chain-store espadrilles. She looked beautiful.

For the millionth time, Diana looked at Miles's childhood playfellow and thought, Why me?

But all she said was, 'You're looking very gorgeous. I take it exotic royalty is in this year?'

Susie laughed. She had very little vanity. And sometimes, when they were not discussing Miles or romantic relationships, she could be very nice, Diana remembered.

'Be honest. You can't see me for the rubies,' she replied.

So she'd been right, Diana thought drily. She hadn't been certain because until she married Miles she had barely seen, much less owned, real jewels.

'They're lovely,' Diana agreed. 'New?'

Susie made a face. 'My grandmother's. We don't ask too closely how *she* got them. Are you ready?'

Diana glanced at her reflection. Normally she didn't wear much make-up but tonight, for some reason, she suddenly felt as if she wanted colour on her face. Armour, she thought wryly. Or maybe camouflage.

'Two minutes,' she said, reaching for the mascara.

Susie sat down on the love-seat. She watched Diana with a strange expression.

'You're beautiful, aren't you?' she said abruptly.

Diana was so startled that she nearly poked the mascara wand in her eye.

'You're joking.'

'No.' It was oddly sombre. 'You have the bones. And that look of vulnerability. As if you'd tremble into dust if a man laid a hand on you. I see why——' She stopped.

Diana turned, incredulous. 'Susie, that's nonsense,' she protested. 'I'm just a standard washed-out English blonde. No features, no colouring. Whereas you——' She gestured eloquently at Susie's ensemble.

Susie's smile was crooked. 'It's all detachable in my case. I *wish* I looked like a sea nymph.'

Diana was startled and more than a little embarrassed.

'You can't mean me. I can't even swim. It was one of the things——' She stopped, biting her lip.

Susie's brow creased. 'One of the things that made Miles feel protective?' she said in a light, hard tone. But there was an undertone to it that, if it hadn't been ridiculous, Diana would have said sounded like pain.

'One of the things that most annoyed him,' she corrected. 'Oh, I don't want to talk about him. Ever since I got off that damned plane, I seem to keep coming back to Miles. Let's drop the subject. And lead me to some food. I'm starving.'

Susie laughed again, her friendliness returning as suddenly as it had evaporated. She stood up. 'Stick close,' she said.

The castle was a jumble of buildings tacked on to the original Venetian fortress. Susie led her up steps, round turrets, down corridors until her head whirled. Diana could hardly believe it when at last they came out on to a ramparted terrace overlooking the sea. In the distance, the sun was setting behind the hills across the bay.

There were three men already on the terrace. Diana stopped dead. An old boyfriend of Susie's, Miles had said. But she had never heard that Dimitri Philippides was anything other than an old family friend. She looked quickly at Susie but the Countess's expression told her nothing.

Dimitri and Christos Galatas were sipping aperitifs. Miles was in the process of lighting a series of perfumed flambeaux. The scented smoke wafted across to them.

He turned, quick as a cat, when they set foot on the terrace. He caught Diana's eye and grinned.

'Against the mosquitoes,' he said as she raised her eyebrows. His voice was easy. For a moment they felt like friends again.

She laughed, tension temporarily forgotten. 'And I was going to congratulate you on a romantic idea.'

Miles grinned. 'Oh, I have those too.'

Diana caught her breath. But the others had not picked up that private, challenging message.

'Not before dinner,' said Chris. 'If you're going to start quoting Homer again, wait until I've had enough brandy to appreciate it. Hi, Diana, how are you?'

Dimitri was already bowing over Diana's hand. They had met before, both during and since her brief marriage. He had always been exquisitely tactful, however, and she liked him.

'Last night Miles gave us Odysseus's return,' he explained now, setting a basketwork chair for her. 'It was very—er—impressive.'

'It was very long,' corrected Count Galatas. He grinned at his friend. 'I keep hoping that his memory will go with advancing years. But it doesn't. Unlike mine,' he added with a sigh.

'That's because I keep it exercised,' Miles said smugly. 'You just sit about in those pets' parlour offices of yours, letting your secretaries do the remembering. You're going soft, Chris.'

Since Count Galatas ran a thriving international commodity business, this seemed unlikely. Chris, anyway, was not put out by these strictures.

'I like to be comfortable,' he said mildly. 'And that includes no narrative poetry until I'm sozzled enough to stand it.' He turned to Diana. 'I hope you had a good journey?'

The words were civil enough but there was none of that affection with which he had spoken to Miles. There never had been. From Chris Galatas's point of view his friend's new wife had always been an unknown quantity. She had never managed to prove herself. If he had conspired to get her and Miles here together, Diana thought suddenly, it must have gone against the grain with him.

She had wondered in the beginning whether it was some sort of influence from Chris that had persuaded Miles to leave her. Chris was currently on his third wife, an elegant woman with whom he spent the shortest possible time, and he did not have much use for women. Diana was pretty sure that Chris would have preferred Miles not to marry at all; to stay a free spirit. And if that was hopeless then he wanted him as a brother-in-law, not married to some English nobody.

She'd dismissed the thought soon enough, of course. Who knew better than she did that Miles had never been influenced by anybody? He did what he wanted—including discarding a wife who had become an encumbrance.

In the corner of the terrace a barbecue was glowing. Having tended his candles, Miles went to it.

'I'm chef this evening,' he announced to the company at large.

Chris groaned. 'Susie...'

But Susie was laughing. 'Oh, let him, Chris. You know he'll only criticise mercilessly if you or I do it.'

'Nobody cooks kebabs the way I do,' Miles agreed modestly.

Chris sniffed. 'Raw.'

'Rare,' corrected Miles, grinning. 'And properly marinated.'

Dimitri turned to Diana. 'We had them last night. I hope you like garlic?' he added with feeling.

Before she could answer, Miles sent her a flashing smile across the glowing coals.

'She learned to,' he said softly.

Dimitri looked startled. A well-shaped eyebrow flicked up.

Diana felt her cheeks burn in the darkness. She hastened to give them a cool explanation.

'Before I went to university I led a very sheltered life. I'd never even been to France. So—no garlic.' It struck just the right note of rueful amusement, she thought, pleased. And it made Miles frown quickly, which was even more pleasing.

Christos, who spent most of his working life in Paris, looked intrigued.

'How is that? I thought the English were in and out of France all the time.'

'Not,' said Diana drily, 'the rural working classes.'

Christos continued to look puzzled. 'But surely—those school trips that your educationalists are so proud of. Didn't you go to France with your school? To learn the language?'

Diana caught Miles looking at her speculatively. When they were married he had never discussed her background with his friends. He said she was too sensitive about it. But he had respected her wish and not referred to it. It was something she had corrected since.

She lifted her chin. Well, to all intents and purposes their marriage was over now. If her lowly ancestry upset them, it couldn't reflect on Miles any more.

'School trips take place during the holidays,' she said quietly. 'Or they did at my school. In the holidays I had to work.'

Chris said, 'Work? Oh, you English and your discipline! But surely it would have been work learning French in France?'

Diana smiled. 'Work to earn my bread,' she explained gently. 'My father was a gardener on a big estate. My mother did housework in the big house. My father had an accident and couldn't go on working. They let us keep the cottage but it was still difficult on just my mother's wages. I shouldn't really have stayed at school after sixteen but I was clever and they both wanted me to. So——' she shrugged '—we compromised. I stayed on and did my exams and took jobs in the holidays. So it was a long time before I encountered snails and garlic butter.'

There was a queer little silence. They were all looking at her as if she had sprouted two heads. All except Miles. He knew it all already, of course. And had his own views of her relationship with her parents.

'Tied to your mother's apron strings,' he had flung at her more than once.

She met his eyes now in the flickering candle-light. He was inscrutable.

Susie broke the silence. 'Well, there are no snails on the menu tonight. Only salad and the kebabs that Miles marinated in some poison of his own. Though, I grant you, that's probably eighty per cent garlic.'

They all laughed. Miles, Diana remembered with a pang, had always been a better cook than she was. Whatever he bothered to do, he did to masterpiece standards, of course. And tonight, true to form, he produced an excellent meal.

Dimitri filled Diana's plate and made sure her wine glass was topped up. In fact she would have preferred water but it seemed churlish to say so amid the general cordiality.

So Diana was feeling a little light-headed when Christos began to mutter over the brewing of Greek coffee. She had drunk it before and knew how to avoid the river silt at the bottom. But Christos was clearly adding vast amounts of sugar. So she refused it and continued to sip her resinated wine.

Under the cover of general conversation Miles said in her ear, 'Don't you think you've had enough?'

Diana jumped and half turned in her chair. He was kneeling just behind her chair, relighting a candle and using her as a wind-break to shield the flame from the light breeze that had sprung up with nightfall. She looked down at him haughtily.

'You've no head for it,' he reminded her pleasantly. 'As well you know. And if you carry on like this, Don Juan in the silk shirt over there is going to have lots of fun putting you to bed.'

She glared at him. Dimitri's exquisite grey shirt very probably was made of silk. It infuriated her that Miles should notice and mock him for it.

'Don't be disgusting.'

Miles looked pleased with himself. 'Don't want him to, Di?'

'That's not what I meant,' she began, recognising deep waters too late.

But he stopped her with that knowing, lop-sided smile of his.

'It's what you said. *I* don't think you fancy Don Juan half as much as you think you do.'

'I——' Diana bit her lip.

He had her boxed into a corner. If she told the truth, and said that she and Dimitri were not interested in each other, Miles would take it as a personal victory. But if she dissembled he was equally capable of calling Dimitri over from his conversation with Christos and telling him to take Diana to bed because she was tired.

She said fiercely, 'I hate you, Miles.'

He put his head on one side. The candle-flame threw the strong bones of his face into dramatic relief. For a moment he looked like a satyr—calculating and mischievous and quite heartless. His eyes were laughing but there was a distinct challenge in their depths.

'Now there you probably *do* know how you feel,' he allowed.

Her hands clenched round the stem of the Galatas family crystal. It was better than hitting the smile off his face and causing a scene.

'Not without cause,' she hissed under her breath.

The candle-flames were making little devils dance in his eyes. In the darkness they were as black as molasses, except for those little points of flame.

'That's a matter of opinion,' he countered. 'Some people would say I was a model ex-husband.'

Diana gasped. His smile grew.

'Generous,' he went on. 'Unobtrusive. Tolerant.'

'*Tolerant*? You?'

'Not a word of reproach about the way you've been running around the last two years,' Miles said, his voice hardening. 'You've made a good job of turning yourself into a rich man's house guest, haven't you, my pet? Since it was my money that paid for it, I might have been entitled to complain a bit, don't you think? Even put a stop to it, if I chose. But I've been mildness itself, you have to agree.'

Diana stared at him, uncomprehending. He might have been speaking a foreign language for all the sense he was making. She didn't understand him. But she knew that, in spite of the cool air, there was real heat licking through his indifferent tones.

She said in a low voice, 'You know why I took the allowance.'

'Your wheelchair-bound father,' Miles said without inflexion.

Diana said desperately, 'We'd *started* buying that house for them. I couldn't let it go when they'd got everything just where Daddy could use it...'

'Did it ever occur to you to get a job?' Miles asked, his voice deceptively mild. 'You were bright enough, as I recall. You might even have been able to contribute a bit yourself.'

Diana turned further round in the basket chair, staring at him. A *job*? She hadn't had a holiday in two years! 'What are you talking about, Miles?' she asked.

'Or did you think your pathetic struggle to get to university was enough?' His words bit. 'I admire that, of course. I always have admired it. But I don't think I care for the way you seem to have decided that you've had your share of adversity and now the world owes you a living.'

The light, amused voice had an edge like Toledo steel. Diana put her glass down on the terrace very carefully.

'I don't understand,' she said.

'No?'

She turned her head to meet his eyes fiercely. '*No*. I've done nothing... Why attack me like this? Suddenly?'

Their eyes locked with a force like a blow. Diana knew he felt it too; she could see it in the way his mouth twisted. But he was not admitting it.

'Now there's a lot of questions,' he mocked. He stood up. His shadow was long and menacing in the candle-light. 'It's not sudden,' he said with precision. 'It's not an attack. And I'm tired of you doing nothing. I've had enough. I give you fair warning. I'm not going to support you until you find some society playboy to take over your bills. I'm going to take you in hand. It's about time somebody did.'

Diana stood up too. Marriage to Miles had taught her a lot about disguising hurt. She said in a cool, dismissive voice, 'You will do nothing of the kind. I shall leave tomorrow.'

'You won't,' he corrected gently.

The others were moving away from the battlements, Christos pointing at the stars. A lecture on the heavens was clearly in progress. Miles gave her a slow smile. Diana began to wonder if she was going mad.

'You will stay,' he told her. 'And you will listen to me.'

CHAPTER THREE

DIMITRI walked her back down the stairs and passages to her room. He was obviously a frequent visitor. He had quickly grasped, though, that she wasn't, notwithstanding her embarrassing relationship to Miles, who regarded it as a second home.

'Susie thinks she runs the castle,' he told her.

They were strolling along a corridor. Their footsteps echoed queerly off the stone walls. Ridiculously, she knew, Diana was as tense as if they were being followed.

'Nominally it belongs to Miles but...'

This brought her attention smartly back to her companion.

'*Miles*?'

Dimitri gave her a surprised look. Although he had been angelically tactful, he was well aware that she and Miles had been married and were no longer.

'Didn't you know? He was practically brought up here.'

Diana shook her head. 'I knew that. His parents travelled all the time and Count Galatas was his godfather. I didn't know he had any claim...'

Dimitri made a rude noise. 'Godfather, my eye.'

Diana halted, staring at him. 'What do you mean?'

Dimitri looked faintly annoyed with himself. Then he shrugged.

'Well, if I don't tell you someone else will. I'm surprised they haven't already. Especially as you're here.' He paused and then said as if he were weighing his words, 'The old Count had two sons, you know. The good brother who stayed at home and made money. Well, some of the time. Chris and Susie's father. And the bad brother who ran away to sea.'

Diana was bewildered.

'And was never heard of again?' she prompted, when he stopped.

'Oh, he was heard of all right. From all over the world. Sydney, Rio. New York. Valparaiso. You name it, Conrad went there. Or so my mother says,' he added conscientiously. 'He was—er—a free spirit.'

Diana began to see where this was leading. She drew a careful breath.

'And Miles was the result—according to your mother? Where?'

Dimitri cast her a look of mingled respect and deprecation. 'South America somewhere. He was a real nomad, Conrad. An explorer. Anne Tabard was a diplomat's wife or something. In some God-forsaken, mosquito-infested frontier town on the edge of the rainforest. Her husband was a lot older, I believe.'

Diana had met Lady Tabard. She examined her recollection of her ferociously sophisticated mother-in-law and found she didn't believe it.

'She must have been very bored,' Dimitri mused. Clearly he found it difficult to reconcile the two images as well. 'And Conrad was lethal with the ladies. A real heartbreaker, according to my mama.' He slanted a look down at her. 'She says he was exactly like your Miles.'

Diana did not rise to any one of the number of lures in that last, casual remark. Instead she said coolly, 'Is this all conjecture, or is there any proof? Does anyone know what happened?'

Dimitri shrugged. 'Conrad stayed with the Tabards on his way up the Amazon looking for some lost tribe.

There are letters, I believe. One imagines they had an affair before he went up-river.'

Diana shivered. 'Why didn't she go with him?' she said, half to herself. A sudden thought struck her. 'Or did she?'

Dimitri was astonished. 'From what I hear she wanted to get *out* of the place, not deeper into it. And Conrad wouldn't have been a good bet. He was always disappearing up glaciers and across oceans single-handed.'

Diana shook her head. For the first time she felt the stirring of some sympathy for her icy mother-in-law.

'Was there a scandal?'

Dimitri laughed. 'From the English? My dear, you have to be joking. Her husband was completely civilised. Conrad was nowhere to be found, of course. So old Galatas did the decent thing. Nothing acknowledged, needless to say, but there was always discreet support. The Tabards weren't well off. And eventually, all three got a share of the inheritance. Miles was particularly fond of the castle. So he got it. Chris got the fleet and the commodities business. Susie got shares and the jewellery.'

Diana felt strangely chilled. Half of her did not believe the story. She didn't want to believe it. Miles hadn't told her and surely he would have—at least in the days when they were close? Yet for some reason half of her found it all too convincing.

'What happened to him?' she asked at last. 'To——' she found she couldn't call him Miles's father '—to Conrad?'

Dimitri made a face. 'Who knows? He could be ruling some lost tribe somewhere. Or he could be dead. I don't think the family ever hear from him, anyway.'

Did Miles? Diana faced the thought painfully. He had never hinted at it. But then how much else of his private history had he withheld from her? She had told him everything and—— She caught her breath at the wave of desolation that swept over her.

Still, she thought. It made her angry. She ought to have got over it. She ought to be impervious to revelations about Miles Tabard by now. He was nothing to do with her any more. Was he?

Hastily, she said goodnight to Dimitri at her bedroom door. She was almost absent about it and his ironic look brought her up short. It had not occurred to her that he might want to kiss her goodnight. His expression told her that he had noticed. She closed her door in some confusion.

She went to the window. It was absolutely dark. She opened the french windows quietly. At once the honeyed scent of jasmine engulfed her. She stood very still. She could just make out the shapes of formal tubs which would no doubt hold geraniums. In the distance she could make out flashes of phosphorescence from the sea. She leaned her temple against the edge of the door, savouring the scents, the stillness, the distant lulling hush of the bay.

Why had Miles not told her? She could not believe he was ashamed. He wasn't ashamed of anything. He looked the world in the eye and dared it to criticise him.

Had Anne Tabard sworn him to secrecy? But other people seemed to know. Did he think it was none of Diana's business? Or had he thought it would give her a hold over him he didn't want her to have? The last possibility chilled her.

She rubbed her face tiredly against the frame. Or wasn't it true after all?

Dimitri and the Galatas family inhabited a social circle as small in its way as a village. Oh, they jetted all round the world but they met the same few people in each exotic stop-over. Like any other small community, they thrived on gossip, not all of it true. Maybe Dimitri's mother, seeing Miles's intimacy with the Galatas grandchildren, had put two and two together to make five.

And yet ... And yet ...

There was a sound below her. Diana froze.

The terrace was a long eighteenth-century affair that swept the length of one façade of the castle. Shallow steps led down not to a formal lawn, but an incongruous olive grove. Diana had seen it briefly earlier. Now she could just make out the trees in the dark. Trees and nothing else. The noise came again.

Silent-footed, she went outside to the edge of the terrace. Hands braced lightly on the marble balustrade, she scanned the shadows. It could have been some small animal. A lizard, say, although she had the vague idea that they were usually silent. Or——

She saw the pale gleam of a shirt-front among the trees and drew a sharp breath.

'Did I disturb you?' said Miles softly.

When didn't he disturb her? Especially coming at her without warning out of the scented night. He must have eyes like a cat's to make her out in this blackness, thought Diana. She found she was shaking.

'You gave me the fright of my life,' she spat back, finding her voice. 'I was just trying to convince myself that there were hedgehogs in Greece. Noisy hedgehogs.'

'I must be losing my touch.' The husky voice was amused.

He came out of the trees and ran lithely up the steps. His feet made no sound. He stopped in front of her. He didn't touch her.

'There was a time I could have got into any room off the terrace and not a soul would have heard me,' he told her softly in her ear.

Diana stepped back. 'Excellent talent for a cat burglar. Surely wasted on a physicist?' she responded tartly.

Her breathing was hurried. Deliberately she steadied herself. She saw his teeth gleam in the dark.

'Ah, but in those days physicist wasn't on my list. Too mundane. I was going to be a rock star. Jet pilot. Explorer.'

She was startled into a little laugh.

'What, *all* of them?'

'All of them,' he assured her solemnly. 'Maybe a brain surgeon in my spare time. Brain surgeons seemed to go down well.'

'Down well with whom?' Diana began, and found that he had moved imperceptibly so that now he was a good deal closer than she had realised.

'Use your imagination,' he told her huskily.

Her mouth was suddenly dry.

'Are you telling me you planned on being a vile seducer when you grew up?' she said, trying for a tone as cool and amused as his own. She didn't, she thought critically, do too badly either.

'Not vile,' he demurred.

He took another step forward. This time she saw it. She moved sideways and came up hard against a jasmine-entwined pillar. She put a hand against the cool marble to steady herself.

'I'm relieved to hear it,' she said politely.

'You ought to know without being told.' He was reproachful.

Diana flinched. She knew she was being teased. It was almost unbelievable. But she knew that provocative tone. She took firmer hold of her supporting pillar.

'I,' she told him lightly, 'never knew you in your midnight seducer days.'

'You missed something.' He was still laughing at her. In spite of the blackness of the night, she could feel his eyes on her, as vividly as a touch or the light breeze eddying up from the sea. She moved restively.

'I'm sure. I——'

'Mind you, getting out of the olive grove on to the terrace, without being caught, was only Phase One,' Miles said thoughtfully. 'And I seem to be out of practice there.' He reached for her. 'Let's see how we go on Phase Two.'

Phase Two had Diana breathless and shaking in seconds.

'Ah,' said Miles complacently, raising his head. 'It all comes back. Just like riding a bike.'

'Take your hands off me,' said Diana. She heard the tremor in her voice and despised herself for it.

'Keep your voice down. You don't want to wake the household.'

'I don't care if I wake the dead,' said Diana, really shaken. 'Take your hands off me *now*.'

Miles complied. His hands, she noticed, showed no disposition to linger. But he wasn't at all put out of countenance either.

'The trouble with you,' he said mildly, 'is you have no spirit of enquiry.'

Diana pushed past him. She took up a defensive stand behind a basket-weave chair, clutching its scratchy back like a lifebelt, and turned on him.

'I've plenty of spirit of enquiry,' she said grimly. 'Like what the *hell* you think you're doing, for a start.'

He gave a soft laugh. 'Me? I'd have thought I was easy enough to read. Reviving memories. Calling on my wife.'

'Ex-wife,' she interjected swiftly.

'Nope.' In the dark she could just make out the movement of the dark red hair. 'Not yet.'

She dismissed that with a gesture.

'Only because your damned solicitor was so inefficient he couldn't find you to sign the papers.'

Miles laughed again, quite kindly. It chilled her blood.

'Honey child, why do you think that was? I haven't been on the moon.'

Her heart gave a great thump like a pile-driver. Instinctively she put her hand to her side.

'I—don't understand.'

'He had instructions not to find me,' Miles said coolly, watching her.

For the second time that day, Diana felt the ground lurch under her.

'But—but why?' she managed at last. 'You were the one who left. You must want a divorce.'

'Is that why you asked for one?' he said swiftly.

Two years alone and the harsh months before them had taught Diana how to evade questions like that.

'Are you deliberately trying to be bloody-minded, Miles?' she demanded.

Yet again he disconcerted her. He propped himself against the balustrade and said thoughtfully, 'That's part of it, I suppose. The male need to look out for his own.'

She had a sudden vision of Dimitri's ironic look when she wished him goodnight and had an unwelcome revelation.

'Did you come here to make sure I was on my own tonight?' she said, furious. She saw his shoulders lift, and said between her teeth, 'I am not your own, Miles Tabard. I never will be.'

Again. She didn't say it. She didn't have to. It lay between them almost tangibly. She couldn't look at that casual, lounging body without remembering how completely she had been his own—once.

He remembered too, it was clear.

'No?' he said softly.

Diana felt as if she were in a whirlwind. 'I don't *understand* you,' she said in despair.

There was a pause. Then he said, 'I can see that. You don't know me very well, do you, Di?'

She winced. 'Did you ever let me know you?' she flashed.

Miles ignored that. 'You thought I'd let it go on forever? All this running around Europe after rich men. This great house. That palace. Do you ever go out with anyone who isn't a three-swimming-pool man, these days?'

If it hadn't been so hurtful, it would have been funny. Her job took her to the historic houses of Europe and the States; but, if their owners ever showed any personal interest in her, Diana Tabard was known for packing her bags and leaving.

There hadn't been anyone for her since Miles left. In her heart of hearts she knew there wouldn't be. It had hurt too much to risk again. But she wasn't going to tell Miles that.

She said in a strangled voice, 'You have no right to criticise the way I live.'

'You used to want to teach.' His voice was gentle, almost sad. 'Couldn't you have gone back to it?'

'When you left me, you mean?' Diana gave a hard laugh. 'I had to do something and I'd been out of university too long for a job to come up just like that. You didn't want me to stay on after we married.'

'So it's my fault?' He sounded resigned. 'I might have guessed.'

Diana flinched. 'It's nobody's fault,' she said in a voice like ice. 'It just happened. And I had to make the best of a bad job.'

He moved. 'You really think that is the best?'

Diana thought of the long hours, the travelling, matching colours till her eyes ached, the arduous processes of reconstructing paint and fabric.

'It's no picnic,' she allowed.

'Look,' Miles said in his most reasonable tone, 'give me a week of your time. Carry on with your holiday. Unwind. Take stock. If after that you want to carry on the way you are—well, it'll be your business. Only,' his voice grew grim, 'you won't do it on my money.'

Diana was instantly tense. 'The allowance...'

'Stops,' Miles said succinctly.

Diana thought of her parents' delight in their small house with its purpose-designed kitchen where her father could reach things and his conservatory where he could grow his plants. It was their independence which was at risk. She was building up a reputation as a consultant in her field but it was a slow business. She was almost sure she wouldn't be able to meet the payments on their mortgage out of her present income.

She said, 'What if I go tomorrow?'

'Then the allowance stops tomorrow,' Miles said, quite gently.

It was no choice at all. They both knew it.

He had always been like that, she thought with a flash of unwelcome memory. He didn't fight. He didn't even seem to *care* most of the time. But without raising his voice or taking any sort of stance he simply made it impossible for her to do anything except what he wanted.

He came over to her and took the light basket-weave chair out of her hands. She jumped. He bent and kissed her mouth lightly, almost insultingly. Diana went rigid.

Miles gave a soft laugh. He patted her cheek. He meant to denigrate her and he succeeded. Diana gave a small sound of protest.

'Quite right. Not a swimming-pool to my name; you'll have to change the entrance qualification,' he drawled.

And then his arms were round her like bands of steel. His hands in the small of her back hurt. He was kissing her with a bruising strength that was almost frightening. Her skin felt scorched. She struggled. Miles didn't seem to notice.

He had never kissed her like this before, not even when they were astonished by love and still exploring. Not when they were married. She had never been kissed like this in her life. It felt as if he was furiously angry, yet more with himself than her. It felt as if his mouth would sear deep into her and change her forever, as if that was what he was determined to do.

Earlier Diana had felt an electric echo of their old passion for each other. But this was nothing like that. Diana felt herself sinking in a sea of fire, appalled and helpless.

'*No*,' she said. She didn't know if she was addressing Miles or herself.

He let her go as abruptly as he had seized her. Diana fell back. Her mouth throbbed. Her whole body throbbed. Two years of careful independence and painfully cultivated poise cracked wide open in a moment, she thought. Her hands flew to hide her burning cheeks as she backed away from him.

'Don't ever do that again,' she said in a voice she barely recognised as her own.

He took a hasty step after her. Instinctively her hands went out to ward him off. He stopped dead. She could not look at him. She had the impression that he was willing her to do so with every atom of his considerable personality. But she wouldn't give in.

She heard him draw a careful breath. 'Di,' he said in an undertone.

Her chin went up. 'You've made your point.'

He was preserving a careful distance. 'And what point is that?'

'That you still have—power—over me.' Her voice shook. The admission humiliated her and it was a worse humiliation that Miles would know it.

'Di,' he said again, softly.

'Get away from me.' There was real fear in her voice, fear of losing the last of her fragile self-possession.

He hesitated. She saw him debate and tensed. She saw him take that in, too, and fling up his hands, palms open.

'*Hell,*' he said explosively.

Before she realised, he turned on his heel and was running silently down the marble steps. He disappeared into the aromatic shadows while she was still fighting for composure.

It was not, Diana acknowledged wryly to her mirror the next morning, the most restful night of her life. In spite of her tiredness and the wine, her mind could not relax. Round and round it went: indignation at Miles's assumption about her life; bewilderment at how he arrived at his conclusions; fear that he would take action which would cost her parents their haven; indignation again that she should be caught in this trap.

Would he carry out his threat? It wasn't like him to be vindictive. But then two years of marriage had taught her that Miles didn't threaten anything he wasn't prepared to do. She must talk to him. Abandon her pride—and heaven knew there wasn't much of that left after last night—and make him understand the truth about her visits to the grand houses, since he seemed to resent them so much. Explain about her job. Then maybe Miles would apologise and they could say goodbye.

Miles? her wiser self said tartly. Miles, *apologise*?

Two years of marriage had taught her that too. Miles had a simple philosophy: never explain, never apologise. He said it kept life uncomplicated. Perhaps it did, for him. For Diana, trying to guess his mood and assess his intentions in those last months, it had turned the marriage into a living nightmare.

She propped her hand on her chin, studying the too prominent cheekbones in the mirror. She didn't look so bad now. When Miles first walked out she had looked like a ghost.

She'd looked like a ghost the night of the Comem Ball. For weeks Miles had been coming home late, sleeping in his study, spending his weekends with Steve Gilman and his computer.

The only person he had seen outside his work was Susie, in London and signalling an emergency. He had run up to her West End hotel the evening of the day she telephoned. But then he always went when Susie summoned him.

The rest of the time he was so busy that he barely spoke. Diana was astonished when he'd announced that he wanted them to go to his college ball.

Her mouth twisted at the memory. She had tried so hard. She had even asked Susie to take her to her own exclusive dressmaker in London.

The dress was a drift of grey-green voile shot through with the faintest thread of gold. It left her shoulders bare and clung to the point where the skirt swirled at hip height. She had put her hair up for once, letting it curl on to her long neck in feathery curls. Miles loved those curls. Or he had once said he did. She wore the jade drops he had given her as an engagement present.

Once she would have been delighted with the way she looked. But twenty months into marriage with Miles left her standing in front of him waiting for his verdict. The brown eyes had flicked over her once and come to rest on her naked shoulders.

'Did you decide against total nudity because of the temperature?' he asked neutrally. There was not the glimmer of a smile in the question.

Diana was stunned. The hard eyes told her nothing. That was when she sensed dislike for the first time. It was like a blow.

'I'll go and change,' she said quietly.

She put the dress and the jade away and never looked at them again. When she left the Oxford house they were still in their boxes in the bedroom that by that time she and Miles had openly ceased to share.

Yet yesterday—this morning—he had been almost as he was when they first met. He had laughed and teased her. He had made her feel—well, when she walked in on him in that bed and realised who it was, he had made her feel as if the years between were all in her imagination. As if he and she belonged together and had never been seriously apart.

'Careful,' Diana said to her mirrored image softly. 'Be very careful. You can't afford to be taken in again.'

There was a perfunctory scratch on the door. She looked up, startled. To her astonishment, Susie Galatas walked in bearing a tray.

'Maria said you were still asleep when she looked in. I thought you might like breakfast.' There was a constraint there. But it sounded as if she was genuinely trying to be friendly.

The tray was piled high with rolls. There was yoghurt too and a silver dish of honey as well as a steaming pot of coffee. Two cups. Susie—or someone—was intending to stay.

Diana swung round on her stool, her eyebrows lifting.

'Lavish,' she commented.

'Well, you ate little enough last night,' Susie said. She sent her guest a slant-eyed look. 'Did you think Miles had poisoned the food?'

Not that friendly, then. Diana side-stepped it with the ease of practice.

'Tiredness. I've been travelling too long.'

Susie poured coffee for both of them and took hers to the chaise-longue, tucking her feet under her.

'How was Hamburg?' she asked.

'Wet. But it should be rewarding.'

Susie nodded absently. 'It worries you that Miles is here, doesn't it?'

Diana made a great business of helping herself to yoghurt and swirling the dark golden honey into it.

'He's entitled,' she said carefully.

'But you're not happy about it.'

Diana avoided her eyes. Even if she knew what the truth was about her complicated feelings for Miles, she didn't feel like sharing them with Susie Galatas.

So she shrugged. 'He's human. We used to get on well enough, after all.'

Susie's eyes widened. 'You mean you'd go back to him?' she said blankly. 'After all you've said?'

Diana took a spoonful of yoghurt, not answering.

Susie looked troubled. 'Oh, God. It must be hell for you, being here with him. Look—if you want to go, I'll tell him. We won't be offended. Honestly.'

Yesterday, it would have been all that Diana needed to have her turned round and out of Castle Galatas in minutes. But Miles with his damnable blackmail had effectively cut off that escape route.

So she said casually, 'I can handle it.' She gave Susie a warm smile that was almost genuine. 'I'm going to snooze and rest, whenever I'm not working. If I know Miles he'll be flinging himself round the bay in a boat. Or running the marathon. We won't meet except at meals.'

Susie sucked in her bottom lip, shaking her head.

'For instance,' said Diana, taking more coffee, 'today, I'm going to lie on the terrace and not lift a finger all morning.'

Susie uncurled her legs and stood up. She still looked worried but there was an unusual gleam of amusement there too.

'Oh, no, you're not,' she said. 'Miles is taking us all fishing.'

Diana didn't resist, in the end. At least they would not be alone. Though the relief was short-lived when she saw the amount of luggage Susie and Chris considered essential for the trip.

'Good lord, are you going to *sleep* on board?' Diana demanded.

Dimitri, who was nearest, looked up and grinned. He took her hand and bent briefly over it. 'This is what the brother and sister Galatas consider essential fare for a civilised fishing trip,' he explained.

'The emphasis,' said Chris calmly, 'is on civilised. I am not Miles.'

Miles raised his brows. It fell to Susie to explain.

'Miles likes to kill his lunch,' she told Diana.

'I like my fish fresh,' Miles said.

Susie patted his arm. 'Squid still squirming. We know. We remember.'

They must do, thought Diana. A momentary bleakness touched her. A shared childhood gave an intimacy that nothing else quite matched. She shook off the shadow. 'Can I help?'

'Only by sitting and looking beautiful,' Susie said generously. 'Somebody needs to.'

'And you qualify,' Dimitri told her.

Susie turned away to supervise the picnic basket. Diana smiled. Her jeans were new, only because she had split her old ones climbing over antique fireplaces in Hamburg. Her striped blue shirt and bright scarf came from a chain-store and she wore neither make-up nor jewellery. But she did not protest, as she once would have done. She had learned that compliments were the social coinage with which men like Dimitri negotiated with the opposite sex. They were graceful and quite meaningless.

She saw Miles watching her frowningly. She lifted her chin and aimed a smile somewhere to his left.

'Can't I at least help carry this stuff to the boat?' she asked.

There was a general shout of laughter in which even Miles joined.

'I said civilised,' Chris reminded her. 'There's a hoist to get this stuff down to the bay. My grandfather had it installed.'

'And you and Miles rode up and down on it all week,' Susie recalled. '*How* angry he was!'

Once again Diana felt excluded. She covered up quickly.

'I'm going to be a complete passenger. You're not going to let me contribute at all.'

'Oh, we'll think of something,' Miles murmured.

Dimitri and Chris were hauling a rope tight while Maria and another girl were carefully stowing bottles in a wicker basket. Clearly nobody but Diana was intended to hear the barbed remark.

She looked at him then, schooling her expression. He looked friendly enough on the surface. But the brown eyes were masked. She knew that look. She had hoped—prayed—she would never have to see it again. Her heart sank.

And then, for some reason, she looked at Susie. She was watching them. Susie's beauty was always dark and dramatic but for a moment she looked almost ugly. Her mouth thinned, leaving her looking drained and shockingly old.

She must have overheard Miles's remark too. Diana realised it with a little shock. Heard it and been hurt by it. So Susie must still be in love with him.

She felt a brief spur of anger at Miles. Whether the rumours about him and Susie were justified or not, there was no need to hurt her gratuitously. Diana moved away from him unobtrusively, turning her back. She could feel his eyes between her shoulder-blades, though.

The others seemed unaware. They set off down the path to the boat, Miles first way out in front, then Susie with Dimitri and, last, Diana beside Christos. The other three talked of islands and charts and winds. She allowed her attention to wander.

It was very hot but the others had all brought jerseys, looped about them over long-sleeved shirts. All but Miles, who was wearing the lightest of T-shirts and looked as if he might tear it off at any moment. She watched him springing lithely down the uneven path. He looked superbly fit.

Not for the first time, Diana wondered what he was doing in Greece in May. He had said—hadn't he?—that he had been working in the open air. She had inferred that meant he had been there for some time. Whereas his lawyer thought he was in Australia on a lecture tour.

Had something gone wrong? She watched the solitary figure forging ahead as if impatient with the others' recreational pace. She had deliberately not kept up with his old friends in Oxford, but she had read that his book had been well received and that he and Steve Gilman were being given all sorts of honours in the scientific world. Nothing wrong there, surely?

Of course he drove himself and everyone else at a punishing pace. Diana wondered briefly if that had finally brought about a physical collapse. But she discarded the idea as soon as it was born. Quite apart from the muscular shoulders and the outdoor tan, it was no invalid who was leaping down the path like an Olympic runner.

Abruptly she caught herself. Well or ill, Miles Tabard was no longer any affair of hers. She reminded herself of that all the way down to the boat.

CHAPTER FOUR

THE boat trip was a revelation on a number of fronts, not all of them encouraging. For one thing Diana was surprised to see how relaxed and friendly Chris Galatas was. She thought wryly that it was probably because she and Miles were clearly no longer together.

For another, she was startled and dismayed to find how her heart quivered every time Miles leaped nimbly across the side of the boat. Had he always been this reckless? She watched him scramble over the top of the cockpit in the swaying launch as it curved round the bay, and had the sensation of being in a nightmare. He never seemed to lose his balance, even for a moment, but she found she couldn't bear to watch him.

He's nothing to do with me, Diana told herself again. She felt sick. She turned her back and concentrated on her conversation with Christos.

He was saying casually, 'I hear you're doing up Dieter's place, aren't you?'

The Hamburg client. Of course, she should have realised that Chris would know him. There were swift footsteps which she was almost sure were Miles running across the sloping roof. She swallowed, not looking round.

'I deal with the architect,' Diana said.

Christos took out some sunglasses and pushed them up his Roman nose. He grinned. 'I'm squashed. But I've known Dieter Schleger for a long time.'

Diana eyed him warily. 'What's that supposed to mean?'

'That if there was a gorgeous female tripping about renovating his crumbling tax-loss he'd be hot in pursuit.'

Against her will, she smiled. He was quite right about the reason for Schleger's purchase of his baroque mansion. The architect was open about it.

'I'm flattered,' she said with composure. 'But Herr Schleger doesn't know I exist.' She sat back, clasping her hands round her knees and looked at him thoughtfully. 'You and Miles seem to have an odd idea about what I do. I don't dine in diamonds and satin with the owners of the houses I work on, you know. I'm just as much a workman as the plumber or the person who puts tiles on their roofs. I wouldn't want it any other way. And I've never even *seen* your friend Dieter.'

Chris folded his hands over his stomach. A small smile played about his mouth. 'Wrong idea indeed.' He flicked her a look. 'I hope you won't mind having dinner with the owners here?' he added drily.

'Since you're so democratic in Greece, I'll make an exception,' she said demurely.

Chris gave a great shout of laughter.

Miles came sure-footedly down the deck towards them. As Diana had somehow known he would, he had discarded his T-shirt. His shoulders were as brown as polished walnut. The dusting of hair that formed a triangle on his chest had bleached to auburn. The bone and muscles beneath moved like oiled steel as he put one hand on the side and vaulted down to join them.

Diana caught her breath. One unprepared glimpse of the elegant machine that was her husband's body set her pulses hammering. She fumbled for her own dark glasses.

Miles smiled at her. 'Dazzled?'

For a moment she thought he had noticed her shameful reaction to his near-nakedness and was mocking her. She stiffened, angry and obscurely wounded. Miles's eyebrows rose. Then, too late, she realised he was talking about the gleam of silver where the sun hit the water.

She pushed the sunglasses on with jerky movements, not answering.

Oblivious of the tension, Chris said, 'Not surprising. She's been locked in dark palaces for the last year. Needs the fresh air and sunshine.'

Miles laughed. 'Back to nature, that's what you need.'

Chris said, 'Not too far back. You be careful,' he urged Diana. 'He'll have you climbing masts and eating seaweed.'

Diana's confusion was under control now. 'So I gather,' she said coolly. From behind the protection of her dark glasses she said to Miles, 'When did you develop this Boy Scout streak?'

Miles eased himself down beside her. He spread his arms along the side of the boat, stretching behind her. It was the merest brushing of flesh against the material of her shirt. Diana went still. The warm skin felt like fire against the masking cotton. She felt his eyes on her.

'Oh, it's always been there,' he said easily. 'You didn't see it in England because I don't like wet tents and sausages.'

Chris shuddered. 'I don't understand English education.'

Miles kicked him with a bare, bronzed foot. 'You don't understand education at all, you philistine. When did you last read a book? All you do is make money. Look to the whole man, my friend. Look to the whole man.'

'I conserve my energies,' Chris said with dignity.

Miles laughed. 'Too right. If your car broke down, how far do you think you could walk?'

Chris grinned suddenly. 'As far as I had to. Shut up, you monster. And stop waving your biceps about. You're not going to make me feel inferior. Or Diana either.'

Miles's laughing eyes surveyed her deliberately.

'Diana's a different kettle of porridge altogether,' he drawled. 'You're just lazy. And if you aren't ashamed you aren't proud of it either. Now, Diana thinks it's a good thing to be frail and let people take care of her. Don't you, sweetheart?'

The attack was unexpected but the weapons weren't. It was what Miles had said on that devastating last night.

'I'm not your insurance policy,' he had said to her with that killing quietness. 'You picked the wrong man for a father substitute.'

Even now, it could still hurt. But she had been on her own since then. She had rebuilt her confidence. Miles was not going to put her down again.

'I thought real men like to take care of women,' she told him sweetly.

Miles gave that crooked, mocking smile she had once feared so much.

'*Real* men like their ladies to be equals,' he said softly.

Diana leaned forward casually, so that she broke that delicate friction between their bodies.

'Desirable behaviour is spearing squid and tightrope-walking on fast launches?' she enquired neutrally.

Even though they were no longer touching, she could feel Miles's body tense as if she had surprised him. Chris was chuckling.

'She's right, you know. You wouldn't like a girl to play your games as well as you do yourself, Miles.'

Diana flung him a grateful smile. Miles reached out a lazy foot and kicked him gently again.

'You're supposed to be on my side,' he complained.

Chris flung up a hand, the stub of his cigar between his fingers.

'Not me. I'm a fully paid-up neutral.'

'You're a fully paid-up coward,' Miles retorted. But there was a smile in his voice.

Why, thought Diana, *why* does he sound so tolerant, so friendly when he's teasing Chris and so cold when it's me?

Chris was smiling too. 'I initiate. I create. I inspire,' he said. 'That's work. I just don't like getting my hands dirty.'

Miles flung back his head and laughed. Chris turned to Diana.

'Do you like getting your hands dirty?' he appealed. 'When you're consorting with your plumbers and tilers and whatever, do you take the tools out of their hands and cover yourself with dirt?'

Miles sat upright suddenly. She felt his arm tense along the wood behind her, even though they were no longer touching.

'It's a fascinating thought,' he drawled. 'Dirt, darling?'

Diana didn't look at him. The endearment was like a touch; her blood leaped at it. Even when she knew it was a mockery of everything they had once felt. Correction, thought Diana wryly; everything she had felt.

'Dust rather than dirt,' she said with an effort. Even without looking at him she could feel Miles's eyes on her.

He said slowly, 'I thought you were an interior decorator. An adviser.'

Diana sent him a brief, carefully unfocused smile over her shoulder. She didn't want to meet his eyes. He was too close.

'When you're talking about restoration, it gets a bit basic, I'm afraid. More than pretty ideas and swatches of materials, anyway.'

'You mean those palaces of yours put you on a daily rate and make you bring your own sandwiches?' His voice was full of unholy amusement.

She made herself laugh a little. 'No sandwiches when I'm examining historic fabrics. But you've basically got the idea.'

Miles chuckled. 'Do you enjoy it?'

Diana considered. It was better than thinking about his uncomfortable nearness.

'Most of the time,' she said honestly. 'I'm getting quite good, which is nice. I'm not very keen on having to sell myself but more work comes in these days from recommedations. And of course,' she added with a flicker of malice she couldn't repress, thinking of his strictures last night, 'you meet a very nice class of person.'

Miles's eyes went blank. She looked full in his face and saw they had gone as brown as madeira, bright as the sunlit sea and quite without expression.

'A very nice class of plumber,' murmured Chris, 'is exactly what this castle needs. If we entertain you royally, do you suppose you could give us an introduction, Diana?'

Before she could answer Susie had come and claimed Miles. It didn't seem to Diana that he went reluctantly. She relaxed her tense shoulders against the side of the boat with an almost audible sigh of relief as he went. But it didn't stop her looking after them with something like regret.

Miles and Susie fished noisily from the side of the boat for the rest of the morning. Dimitri came and sat beside her, pointing out landmarks as they rapidly went past. Chris dozed. From the corner of her eye Diana watched the anglers.

Dimitri followed the direction of her gaze. He stopped talking about the coastal landscape.

'I think this time she's going to get what she wants,' he said softly.

It was obvious what he meant. Diana didn't try to pretend she didn't understand. She looked at Susie's animation and thought she detected a hint of frenzy there. Diana, who knew how Miles could remove himself at a stroke when he felt like it, felt suddenly sorry for her. If Susie wasn't as confident as she looked, Miles could hurt her badly.

'If it is what she wants,' she said.

Dimitri looked at her pityingly. 'Diana, how old are you?' he asked.

'Twenty-six,' she said, startled.

'And you have heaven knows how many degrees and run your own business?'

'Well, sort of,' Diana said cautiously. 'It's not quite as grand as you make it sound but...'

He waved the *caveat* aside. 'No matter. My point is that you have a lot to learn.'

She stared at him. His mouth twisted a little and he said gently, 'You think you're bright. And sophisticated. And up to a point you are. But you're no match for Susie. She can't spell in any language and she wouldn't know how to run a cocktail party without help, much less her own business. But she's got you taped and hog-tied.'

'I don't understand,' said Diana, pardonably.

'No. You wouldn't. Because Susie is a Clever Woman,' Dimitri said, stabbing the air with his finger to make his point. 'And you're not.'

'Thank you,' said Diana, ruffled.

He grinned. 'It's a compliment, you know. Clever Women are manipulators. Men don't like that. When,' he added with sudden gloom, 'we notice it's happening.'

He cast a thoughtful look at the cheerful pair and their fishing lines.

'Now I'd say Susie was being a bit obvious this time. But there's no sign Miles has noticed.'

'Miles,' said Diana with bitterness, 'notices everything.'

Dimitri lit a cigarette. He gave her a faint smile.

'Then we should be in for an interesting time.'

But Susie and Miles seemed in perfect harmony. In fact, as Diana watched, they seem to become more and more of a couple. It was easy to attribute it to their shared childhood, of course, but that was too easy. Miles had shared his childhood with Chris as well and they sparred relentlessly. Most of the time it was good-humoured, but just sometimes Diana thought she heard an edge to the teasing. There was no edge at all when he teased Susie.

And there was no teasing in his voice when he fell into step beside her on the way back from the boat.

'Why did you let me think your job wasn't serious?' he asked.

Diana's shoulders stiffened. 'I don't recall discussing my job with you at all.'

'Precisely.'

'So you leapt to conclusions and I'm to blame?' Diana stopped dead and turned towards him. The dusty stones sputtered under the abrupt movement. 'Would you have believed me if I'd said I was interested in the houses, not the titled owners? When did you ever believe my unsupported word, Miles?' she said with a bitterness she couldn't hide. 'Nobody else thought I was chasing the jet set. Why did you? And I don't notice you apologising,' she added acidly.

He stared at her with a very strange expression.

'You want an apology?' he asked softly, at last.

Diana turned away, feeling somehow defeated. 'I don't want anything,' she said wearily.

'Now that I doubt,' said the quiet voice at her shoulder.

She began to walk again, her shoulders slumping. 'What do you want from me, Miles? I've told you I won't stand in the way of a divorce. You need never see me again. And once my business is really solid I can take over the payments on the house.'

He made a sharp movement. 'That's not important.'

'Isn't it?' She was wry. 'I thought it was the thought of my swanning around Europe on your hard-earned cash that was the cause of this—farce.'

'If you thought that, you've even more to learn than Dimitri thinks,' he told her softly.

She was confused. 'More than . . . ?' Then she understood. 'You were listening. Eavesdropping. On a private conversation.' She was almost incoherent with the rage that consumed her.

Miles was unrepentant. 'You said yourself I notice everything.'

'How dare you? You had no right . . .'

'You're my wife,' he said flatly.

'That doesn't give you the right to spy on me——' she began hotly.

He interrupted, 'Maybe not the right. What about necessity?'

'I don't know what you're talking about,' she cried.

'I know you don't.' He was odiously calm. 'Dimitri was right. A *lot* to learn.'

'I hate you,' she said, knowing it was childish but unable to suppress it.

'Possibly.' He didn't sound concerned.

She flung round on him, stopping again. 'Look, now you know I'm a solid citizen who does a decent job of work for her bread—will you let me go?'

'No.'

She swept on, hardly heeding. 'You wouldn't really let my parents be thrown out of their house. They never did you any harm.'

'I said no.'

Her voice rose. 'You used to like them. And it won't be forever. Just another couple of years.'

'If you leave the castle, the allowance stops,' he said implacably.

Diana gave a little sob. 'How can you be so cruel?'

'To insist you have what is obviously a much needed holiday?' His crooked smile didn't reach his eyes. 'Where's the cruelty in that?'

'I can't bear it,' Diana said involuntarily.

'Yes, you can. You bore it very gracefully today. And you'll continue to do so, if you want that allowance.' His voice softened suddenly. 'Look, all I want is a week. Is that so much to ask? I won't hound you, I promise.'

She looked away.

'I don't seem to have much choice, do I?'

His voice hardened. But all he said was, 'You're learning.'

He was as good as his word. He did not seek her out. And when she said she didn't want to go fishing the next day he was the only one of the group who didn't protest.

Diana should have relaxed. Instead, she got more tense. She found herself jumping at odd noises; looking for him, even when she knew he was out in the bay; waiting. The third night she even locked her bedroom door. There was no need. She was undisturbed.

She spent the mornings going round the apartments that needed restoration. Neither Chris nor Susie showed much interest, to her surprise. She began to wonder uneasily if Dimitri was right when he said the castle belonged to Miles.

It seemed inconceivable that she shouldn't have known. It seemed inconceivable that Miles would have arranged to employ his estranged wife to restore the rooms. But nothing about this visit was going the way she expected. It could be that both the holiday and the commission were Miles's idea. Not that he ever said anything that hinted at it. But Diana remembered all too clearly how good he had always been at keeping his own counsel.

The afternoons, theoretically at least, she spent dozing on the terrace outside her room, under the shade of the vines. In fact she sat and stared unseeingly at the bay, her mind turning over and over old estrangements. It was not restful. She began to look strained.

Oddly enough, it was Chris who remarked on it first. It was at the evening meal on the fourth day of Diana's stay. They were on the battlemented terrace looking over the northern stretch of water. On this occasion they were eating spit-roasted lamb from the kitchen and Maria was waiting on them.

'You're looking tired. Are we working you too hard?' Chris said.

Diana shook her head. 'I enjoy it.'

Miles looked up sharply from his discussion with Susie over the wine.

'Come to any conclusions yet?' Chris asked.

Diana hesitated. 'It's going to cost a lot of money,' she said bluntly.

Miles gave a soft laugh. 'In character.'

Diana tried not to wince. She turned to him slowly. 'I'm sorry?'

He smiled at her innocently. 'She was a very expensive lady, by all accounts. The Princess, I mean.'

She met his eyes and saw a lot more than innocence in them. She wondered if the others did too, and shivered.

Chris said tolerantly, 'Well, she had a lot to compensate for—living here in the middle of nowhere with a chap she didn't really know. And a foreigner.'

'An old foreigner,' Miles reminded him. There was an edge to his voice.

Susie said indignantly, 'He wasn't old. He was forty. You're nearly forty, after all.'

'That made him old enough to be her father,' Miles said evenly.

Something troubled Diana. She said slowly, 'And how old was she? The Princess?'

Susie shrugged. 'Who knows? They didn't exactly have birth certificates. She was the last daughter of the Bey, and his favourite. That was why they were so angry when she helped our ancestor escape. And then ran away with him.'

Miles said, 'Family legend says she was twenty. She could have been three or four years either side of it.'

And I was only just twenty-two when you married me, Diana thought, disturbed.

Chris said easily, 'Well, she must have been a strong character. She created quite a salon, you know. It was some achievement, getting civilised people to come out into the wilds of Greece in the middle of the eighteenth century. But she did it. And collected all that expensive furniture that it's going to cost a fortune to put right.'

He sent Miles a quick look. Diana looked at him searchingly for signs that it was going to be his bill. But Miles, as ever, was inscrutable.

She said, watching him, 'It could. If you want to do it properly.'

Chris made a face. 'What do you mean by properly?'

She hesitated. Did they really want a lecture on restoration techniques?

'Well, take the upholstery. I could get the furniture re-stuffed, mended. But if you want it to last another two hundred years looking as it should, you'd need to re-embroider. It's all skilled hand-work. So it's expensive.'

Susie had been looking at Miles too, she discovered. Now she said suddenly, 'We don't want to turn the Princess's rooms into a museum, you know, Diana. I'm sure you're very skilful but this isn't for show. Just for the family's private satisfaction. There's not limitless money to spend.'

Diana was taken aback. It was friendly enough on the surface but underneath there was more than a hint of annoyance. And had there been the faintest emphasis on the word 'family', pointing out that Diana was an outsider?

She said gently, '*I'm* not spending any money at all, Susie. Or saying that anyone else should.' Across the terrace her eyes met Miles's. 'You asked for my views. There they are.'

Miles lifted one eyebrow and his mouth quirked. He looked carelessly amused. There was something in his eyes, though, that was neither amused nor careless.

Diana rapidly averted her eyes. She looked round at the others steadily. She did not say what she was thinking because it was clear from their expressions that they, like Miles, recognised it: I'm not in your employment and

if you speak to me like that again I won't help any
further.

Susie frowned. But at once she was laughing again.

'Of course. It's frightfully kind of you to spend your
holiday going over our mouldy old rooms.'

Diana chose to accept it as a tacit apology.

'It's as well to realise from the first what a big under-
taking restoration often is. It can get completely out of
hand,' she said.

'Because it's done by enthusiasts, I suppose,' Susie
murmured. 'People with lots of knowledge and degrees
and no common sense.'

So it hadn't been an apology.

Before she could answer, Miles intervened. 'Don't you
like enthusiasts, Susie?' he said lazily.

She gave a husky laugh and put a hand on his arm.
'I like *practical* people, darling. You should know that,'
she said into his eyes.

Her hand with its scattering of jewelled rings looked
very small against the white sleeve of his shirt. It also
looked as if she was very used to touching him. It gave
Diana a queer little stab. She looked away, not wanting
to think about why it hurt.

Chris turned to her. 'Well, you sound eminently practical to me.'

'Oh, she does,' Miles agreed. 'You'd better get her to
take you round the apartments tomorrow and explain
the options.'

Was his tone unduly meaningful? Had Chris just received his orders? Or was she being paranoid? Diana
said at random, 'It's not all in my field. I might mislead
you.'

'Ball-park figures,' Chris said and grinned at her expression. 'Don't look so worried. I'm a rich man.'

'Oh, she knows that,' said Miles, his voice hard. 'Don't you, darling? Or you wouldn't be here.'

There was a nasty little silence. This time Diana knew exactly why she was hurt. It made her angry. What right had he to call her a gold-digger? And what reason?

She said coldly, 'I'm here because I was invited. For a holiday. I don't have to tout for business, Miles. I'm an expert. If the *family*——' and she emphasised it just as Susie had '—want to make the room look pretty, without restoration, then they don't need me. I'm too expensive.'

'Surprise me,' mocked Miles.

But Chris intervened, defusing the anger that sparked between them, barely below the surface.

'We'll talk it through tomorrow. I'm not giving myself indigestion fighting over our heritage at this hour,' he said firmly.

Miles spent the whole meal being impeccably polite. Diana, wincing from barbs that she felt she alone understood, could only be thankful when it ended. She excused herself while Susie and Dimitri were brewing coffee. Miles was watching them critically.

'You said it yourself, Chris. I'm tired: I've got a lot of sleep to catch up on,' she murmured. 'I'll slip away now, if you don't mind. I—er—don't want to break up the party.'

The look he gave her held a good deal of comprehension, she thought. But all he said was, 'Sleep well.'

She lost herself returning to her room. She wasn't particularly worried. Since she'd arrived in the castle, she thought wryly, she never seemed to get where she was going at the first attempt. But she always found her way in the end. She was tranquil about it.

Her tranquility disappeared abruptly when she saw Miles standing in the corridor outside her room.

'What are you doing?' she began.

He turned to look at her. He seemed very tall in the shadowed corridor. His shirt was blindingly white against the deep tan of his throat. His hair was longer than she was used to. It brushed the deep collar, like one of those eighteenth-century dandies whose portraits had surrounded her all morning. Except that he was warm and breathing and there wasn't inches of brocade and velvet between those powerful shoulders and the world, she thought involuntarily. She drew a shaky breath.

He scanned her face. 'You're going to do it, aren't you?' he said slowly.

'I don't know what you mean,' she said.

'Chris. You're going to do his silly little ancestress's boudoir.'

'Your silly little ancestress too,' Diana flashed before she thought.

He put his hands on her shoulders. She went still. He turned her slowly so that her face was turned to the light. The deep-set eyes were unreadable.

'You've caught up with that one, have you?' he murmured. 'I wondered when you would. Yes, it's true. Bastard that I am, I share the genes of the Princess whom George Galatas brought home from Turkey. The enemy in the house.'

There was deep bitterness there. Diana was startled. So startled that she forbore to challenge him on the ownership of the castle and whether he was the one who would be paying for her expert services, for all his clever byplay with Chris.

'What do you mean?' she said instead.

'It isn't quite the romantic story Susie wants to believe, you know. She was a brat and spoilt rotten. Hence the French furniture and the Italian paintings.'

Diana said with an odd breathlessness, 'It's a beautiful set of rooms. I'll be glad to do what I can.'

Miles surveyed her. 'Do you feel empathy with her? The Princess? Do you go in that room and sense her poor little exiled spirit calling you?'

His scorn was like a burn. She flinched inwardly. She would not let him see how it affected her, though.

'No,' she said with composure. 'I go into that room and sense a strong odour of rotting horsehair, just like anyone else.'

He gave a brief, unamused laugh. 'She came to a bad end, you know, the Princess. She drove him too far once too often.'

'I know nothing about her,' Diana said defensively.

'Oh, you should look her up. There's plenty of stuff in the library here. Some of it's even in English. She has had her biographers. Attracted by the romance, of course. When they find out the truth, they tend to lose heart.'

'The truth?' said Diana, suddenly wary.

'That she was a calculating, poisonous bitch. She may have been only twenty but she took poor old George Galatas like a professional.' His voice was bitter.

Diana thought, He doesn't sound as if he's talking about people who have been dead for two hundred years and more.

'He was a quiet soul. Something of a scholar. He wrote rather a good book on the Great Bear. Heaven knows what he was doing on that expedition to Turkey. He was no soldier. He was ransomed, you know. It wasn't a dashing escape. She smuggled herself on board, into his stateroom. It damned nearly caused another war.'

Diana said quietly, 'She must have been very much in love with him.'

His laugh was soft and chillingly cold.

'Oh, I don't think so. She didn't have much of a future at home and she didn't fancy life on her own in Europe. She was used to the best, too. George was the ideal solution. So she seduced him and made him marry her. And then made his life hell.'

Diana thought, He's talking about himself. About us.

She said harshly, 'You've never been seduced in your life.'

'No,' he agreed softly.

Their eyes met. It was almost brutal. Diana gasped. He slanted her a mocking look.

'She came to a bad end, you know. She was killed by brigands. Or that's the story. Her body was found by the roadside anyway. It could have been the lover she thought would take her away with him. Or it could have been George himself.'

Oddly shaken, Diana said, 'That's—horrible.'

He said, 'No more than she deserved, some say.'

She looked at the cold, handsome face. 'Do you believe that?' It was a strangled whisper.

Miles gave a slow smile. 'I believe that very young women can sometimes be careless—shall we say?—about how their activities affect others.'

Diana winced.

'And, whether he did it or not, I think poor old George had suffered enough by the time she died. He was something of a mathematician; he did good work after she went.'

Diana felt as if her heart would stop. She flung up her head defiantly and met the predator's gaze as bravely as she could.

'As you have?' she suggested.

Just for a moment the ice in his eyes moved. It didn't melt but it cracked and shifted to show a volcano of feeling that had her retreating involuntarily before she realised it.

Miles gave a soft laugh. It wasn't a pleasant sound. 'Oh, we're fellows, all right, George and I.'

Diana stared at him, mesmerised. The eyes were like a hawk's, clever and pitiless. He moved. She closed her eyes, then felt his fingers, like fire, against her cold cheek.

'I see you agree with me,' Miles murmured.

He drew her against his body, so that she could feel the height and strength and fierce energy there. And then, quite slowly, he let her go. Bewildered, and more than a little afraid, she opened her eyes. His smile was crooked.

'Interesting,' he said.

His hands dropped. Then, abruptly, he made her a quaint little mock-bow and strode past her without another word.

CHAPTER FIVE

DIANA was shaking when she closed the door of her room. In her wildest imaginings she had never expected that passionate outburst from Miles. She knew it was passion. It was there not just in his words but in every line of his body. She knew his body language very well. She had learned to read it during the long silences that were the graveyard of their marriage.

But passion could be deceptive. She had learned that too.

There was no use trying to sleep. Diana pulled on her pretty cotton night things and opened her windows wider. The night was windless. There wasn't even the faint breeze from the sea she had grown used to. The scent of jasmine lay heavy in the humid air.

The scent triggered her memory. Was it only two nights ago that Miles had come to her out of that olive grove? He had reminded her—briefly and shockingly—of how it felt to be in his arms.

She had thought herself safe after two years of hard-won independence. But one potent reminder of what was lost to her had destroyed all that. Diana clutched her elbows, standing statue-still in the warm air. She no longer felt safe.

She was not still in love with him. She couldn't still be in love with him. It was out of the question.

She had been in love, all right—desperately in love. She had been frightened of how much she loved him. When Miles, against all the odds, seemed to love her, she had hardly dared to believe it.

She sighed. Well, he had said he loved her. They probably meant different things by the words. Certainly he had soon grown bored with what little she had to offer a man of his intellect. He had spent more and more time with his research colleagues.

The only time he'd allowed himself to be diverted, Diana remembered painfully, was when Susie rang him with one of her long, passionate phone calls. He would drop everything then. It was his unsophisticated wife who bored him, not the glamorous childhood friend.

So first he grew bored, then impatient, as Diana grew more and more hesitant, more and more afraid of losing him—and, in the end, downright hostile.

She shivered, remembering. There had been a terrible upsurge of anger. She hadn't seen it coming. She was so bewildered, so miserable that she hardly knew what she wanted any more. And she hadn't been reading him right for days. She had lurched from mistake to mistake, hardly daring to open her mouth, and when she had tried to talk to him about it he had rounded on her with such rage that it had appalled her.

'I'm not your insurance policy,' he had said, looking at her as if he despised her.

She had fled to what had once been their room. By then she'd had sole possession, and it had become her sanctuary from the rage in him she didn't understand. So when he'd come to her there later, she had been utterly unprepared. Unprepared and so vulnerable to his fierce caress.

Diana closed her eyes, not wanting to remember. Not able to block it out.

From somewhere she had mustered the self-respect to ask him to leave. Miles had stopped still as if he had walked into a wall. And then he had turned and was gone. Permanently, as it turned out. Without another word. Diana remembered feeling as if she had fallen off the world.

'*Never* again,' she said out loud.

She had not realised how hurt she still was. Seeing Miles every day was making it all too plain. She was hurt and angry. It was anger that made her retaliate against Miles's every barb, anger and a queer, perverse determination to prove to him she did not care any more.

Diana sighed wryly. All she had succeeded in doing was convincing herself, woundingly, that she did still care.

'I wish to hell I didn't,' she murmured.

She looked at the night sky. It was more overcast than the last one she had looked at. She swallowed. Why had he kissed her like that? Was it planned? The Miles she knew never used to do anything without planning it. Yet she had sensed in that astonishing, passionate moment the other night that he had lost some sort of hold over himself.

He wouldn't like that, she thought. Could that account for his suppressed anger tonight? She shook her head. How could you tell with a cool, guarded man like Miles? How could you tell, even if you loved him?

That stopped her.

'I *don't* love him,' she said aloud.

She went back to bed. But her dreams were troubled and she woke early.

There was no one about. There was not even the smell of coffee in the kitchen, it was so early, though the sun was already warm. Diana decided to risk a cautious exposure to its rays. Perhaps she might be soothed into a doze, making up a little for the sleep she had lost, she thought wryly.

She was not alone. Christos was already there, stretched out on his lounger. He looked up at her approach and, seeing her, stood up.

'Going to risk our sun after all?' he asked.

Diana smiled, indicating her sun-cream. 'Blocked from all its rays, yes.'

Chris set a lounger for her. 'You are so admirably cautious. And well organised,' he remarked.

He returned to his reclining luxury. Diana sank down on to the lounger and closed her eyes. It was possible to doze, after all. Though the images of Miles kept coming back.

Eventually she said softly, 'Chris? Can I ask you something?'

'You can try,' he said drowsily.

'You know Miles better than anyone.'

He turned his head towards her. 'I wouldn't say that,' he murmured, his tone dry.

She shook her head, answering the implicit comment. 'I don't know him at all any more. If I ever did,' she added in a painful undertone. 'I wondered—he seems—oh, I don't know. *Angry* somehow. Is there anything wrong?'

'And you say you don't know him?' Chris shook his head. 'I know what you mean. I've seen it too.' He hesitated. Then, seeming to choose his words with care, he said, 'He tells me he's been overworking.'

Diana listened to the carefully neutral tone.

'Don't you believe him?' she asked.

Chris shrugged. 'Oh, I believe him. He's always overworked, as long as he's lived. It's in his temperament. And it was clear that book of his was going to be the beginning of the work cycle, not the end. He's been flogging round the world lecturing. They both have. I believe the other guy's in hospital. Nervous exhaustion, Miles said.'

'Oh, *no*.' Steve Gilman was an easygoing Devonian whose slow speech hid a lightning mind. Diana would have said he was the most stable man in the world. 'Do you think Miles blames himself?'

Chris shook his head, his mouth tightening. 'I don't know. He hasn't talked about it. Won't tell me anything unless I drag it out of him.'

Diana looked down at her hands. 'Maybe he's told Susie.'

'No,' said Chris unequivocally. 'No, he's not talking. He simply turned up in Greece saying he wanted to work in the fields. And that's all he's said. Except the facts about Gilman. And that only when I pushed him. And,' he added with a glimmer of a smile, 'I'd fed him the best part of a bottle of Armagnac.'

Diana was blank. 'But—what's happening to the lecture tour? Is it over? And what about his research? His work is his life.'

'Not any more,' Chris said grimly.

He swung his legs round and sat up suddenly. He faced her, his arms resting on his knees. He took his sunglasses off and Diana saw that his face was set in worried lines.

'He's done what he said he was going to do, I gather. Ever since he's been here, he's played in the fields. Susie came down to be with him as soon as she heard. My office in Athens is full of telexes from people wanting to get in touch with him. He won't even read them. He hasn't opened a book or sat at a desk since he's been here.'

Diana was horrified. 'But—I've never known him like that.'

'Nor have I,' Chris said heavily. 'I'm told that he has some date to speak in Moscow. Major stuff—unity of the east and west scientific establishments—UN-sponsored. He won't talk about that either. They're frantic to get in touch with him. It's in seven weeks' time. Miles won't even say for certain whether he's going or not. I'd bet the whole of the Galatas line that he hasn't started his paper for it, though.'

'Something's happened,' Diana said with conviction. 'He'd never let people down like that.'

Chris rubbed a hand over his eyes. He looked worried.

'I know. I agree with you. But I can't help thinking...' He trailed off.

'What?'

'There's a streak in our family,' he said slowly. 'We have a taste for danger. Living on the edge. Usually we channel it—making scientific discoveries, punting on commercial risks, like me. But if things go wrong—if we're angry, or indignant about some injustice—it can turn into real recklessness.' He gave her a quick look. 'Miles told you about my uncle Conrad?'

Diana bit her lip. 'That he was Miles's father? I know. Miles didn't tell me, though.'

Chris looked astonished. But all he said was, 'By all accounts he was the worst of the lot. Got a lot of people killed when he lost his temper. My grandfather always said Miles was very like him.'

Diana said, 'Miles isn't reckless.'

'What else do you call his attitude to the Russian lecture? He could be throwing away his whole professional reputation. And he doesn't seem to care a fig.'

'There'll be a reason,' Diana said with conviction. 'Miles doesn't do things without a reason. And his career is the most important thing in his life.'

Chris was watching her narrowly. 'I think—just at the moment—something else must be more important.'

She stared. 'Like what?'

He shrugged. 'How should I know? I've told you, he's not talking to me. I wondered whether he'd discussed it with you.'

Diana flushed in comprehension. She looked away. 'He wouldn't. We're only just polite. You've seen it.'

She looked at him in appeal. He looked back steadily, nibbling one arm of his sunglasses. He said nothing.

'We—we aren't *friends* any more,' she offered desperately.

'It's new to me that you ever were.' Chris's tone was dry.

That hurt. 'You're right, of course,' Diana said in a small voice.

He snorted, his exasperation evident.

'Diana, friends don't tear each other to bits. The man was in love with you. Crazy-deep in love. That also,' he said with precision to her disbelieving expression, 'is a Galatas family characteristic.'

There was a step on the spiral stair that led to the ramparts.

'What is?' said Miles behind them.

Diana was appalled. She felt her face flame. Even though she didn't for a moment believe that Miles had loved her like that—if at all—she could still hear the words echoing in the air. If Miles had heard them he would think she *did* believe and... His inevitable mockery was too terrible to contemplate.

Chris gave her a look of comprehension and turned to Miles.

'Persuading lovely ladies to take their clothes off,' he said with absolute calm and a complete disregard for the truth. 'I've been telling Diana she should borrow one of Susie's bikinis and try to lay the foundations of a tan.'

'She burns,' Miles said coolly. 'Anyway, Susie's clothes wouldn't fit.' There was an indefinable distaste in his voice.

He doesn't want me sharing anything of hers, Diana thought suddenly. She lay back on her lounger, her blush subsiding. She had seen many things in Miles's face when he looked at her, but she had never detected distaste before. It made her feel strange.

Miles looked down at them. 'What about a drink?' he said pleasantly. 'I've just been helping Maria with a new barrel of retsina. It wants tasting.'

No sign there of the wilful recluse Chris had described, Diana thought.

Chris shuddered. 'Retsina is for picnics,' he said firmly. 'We can do better than that, Miles. I'll investigate the cellar. What do you feel like, Diana?'

'I don't want any wine.' Even to herself, her voice sounded unnaturally high and breathless. She saw Miles give her a searching look. 'Mineral water would be nice.'

'Back in a trice,' Chris said. And was gone.

Miles took his lounger. He stretched out at once. Diana watched him.

He was browner than she would have imagined possible with that red hair of his. Close to, she could see tiny freckles across his nose and cheekbones. There was a dusting of them along the backs of the muscular arms as well. She remembered his body so well. Even now she was tempted to lean across and carry one warm palm to her cheek.

Hurriedly she put her arms behind her head.

Miles said idly, 'Were you getting the authorised version on our very own princess?'

Diana said, 'No.' It came out rather short because she was still shaken by that humiliating impulse.

Miles raised his eyebrows. 'Matters nearer home, perhaps?'

'Perhaps.'

He sighed. 'I do wish every conversation didn't turn into a fencing match,' he said drily. 'What were you talking about?'

'Ourselves,' Diana said evasively.

He looked at her sharply. He would recognise the evasion, she knew. He was too intelligent.

'Di—I wish——' He stopped, then said abruptly, 'Come swimming with me this afternoon.'

It was an order, not an invitation. She was oddly shaken by it. They had never swum together before. They had never really holidayed together, she realised. Miles had always been too taken up with his work. And she had never had the confidence to insist.

'I'm not a strong swimmer,' she said.

Miles knew that already. He brushed it aside. 'Then we'll sit in the boat and look at fish.'

Diana said suspiciously, 'No killing things?'

He laughed. 'We kill to eat, you know. You're no vegetarian.'

'I don't go on holiday to kill things,' she said stubbornly.

He grinned. 'All right. No fishing. No big game shooting. That suit you?'

It was so absolutely Miles that in spite of her uneasiness Diana could not prevent herself laughing.

Miles turned his head on the pillow of his lounger. It was very near her own. Too near. She saw his eyes: warm brown and teasing. It was so like the brief, vanished happy time that Diana could have cried.

Her face must have changed because Miles said urgently, 'Don't look like that, love. I'm not a monster. I only want——'

But Diana hardly cared what he wanted when he was looking into her eyes and smiling like that. It was too much of a threat. One healed heart and two years' independence were on the line.

She tore her eyes away and said hurriedly, 'All right. I'll swim.'

He reached for her hand. 'You'll enjoy it.'

She tried to withdraw from his grasp. But he had always been stronger than he looked, and weeks of open-air work had given him a grip like iron. He looked down at their clasped fingers, a small smile playing about his mouth.

She found herself saying on impulse, 'Miles, do you own this place?'

His eyebrows rose. 'Why?' he asked softly. He didn't loose her fingers. 'Does it matter?'

'Yes,' she said, trying fruitlessly to remove her hand.

'Why?' he asked again, his eyes intent.

'Because I feel as if there's some sort of conspiracy with me as the only one who doesn't know what's going on,' Diana said frankly. 'And I don't like it.'

Abruptly he released her.

'I see.'

He was silent for a moment. The steep lids dropped, veiling his expression. Then he shrugged, a brief, devastating movement of tanned shoulders. Diana averted her eyes, swallowing.

'Do you?' she persisted.

'Own the castle? Oh, yes,' Miles said indifferently.

Indignation swamped her other feelings. 'Why?' she demanded.

His smile was crooked. 'Because my grandfather left it to me.'

Diana could have hit him. 'I don't mean that and you know it. Why this elaborate charade? Why make Chris offer me the job here as if it were his house?'

He looked at her curiously. 'Would you have come if you'd known it was mine?'

'Of course not.'

Miles shrugged again. 'There's your answer.'

Diana said through gritted teeth, 'You're impossible. How dare you manipulate me like that?'

Miles said slowly, 'I needed to know——'

'Know what?' she demanded.

The crooked smile was rueful. 'How important the glamour had become, I suppose.'

Diana stared at him, disconcerted. 'What?'

'The glamour of your crumbling palaces. The three-swimming-pool men,' he elaborated. He gave a short laugh. 'My mama married a man she thought was glamorous. When she found he was only an ordinary man after all, she imported some foreign glamour. Specifically, the man who became my father.'

He sounded completely indifferent, Diana thought, shocked. And yet... And yet...

He was not looking at her. His eyes were shadowed, in spite of the immaculately cool voice.

'It must have been the best time of her life. Flying down to Rio to watch him play blackjack, then dancing through the night to Carioca crooners. Then back in his own plane to the marital breakfast table. Real high life.'

Diana said swiftly, 'They don't play a lot of blackjack in my crumbling palaces.'

Miles laughed, but differently, as if he really was amused. 'I should have thought of that.' He reached for her hand again, and Diana let him take it without resistance. 'But people told me you were flitting from rich man to rich man. And I'd seen it before. So I had to be sure.'

'People? Who?'

But he didn't hear her. 'You can't blame me for being—concerned. Rich men and castles. I know more about that sort of life than you can begin to imagine. And, believe me, it's not for you.'

Diana stared at him, half puzzled, half affronted. Was he warning her off her friendship with the Galatas family?

'Not for working girls?' she asked sweetly.

'Not for a girl who likes order and stability,' he said quietly.

'As I had when I was married to you?' she gibed.

He winced, letting go of her hand. Diana snatched it back and stood up. How dared he patronise her? From somewhere a volcano of rage seemed to be pushing at the top of her head. She stopped fighting it.

'From what I hear you haven't been exactly a model of order and stability these last weeks—have you, Miles? Dishonoured commitments and unwritten papers,' she said savagely. 'Don't you dare preach to me, you—you playboy. Don't you *dare*.'

He stood up too. Unforgivably, he was laughing. 'Playboy? Darling...'

But she could hear Chris coming up the steps again. It sounded as if Susie and Dimitri were with him. With her flushed face and over-bright eyes, Diana knew she couldn't face them. Especially not with Miles standing there looking like a laughing devil.

She turned on her heel and fled.

She managed to compose herself for lunch. But she was quiet and kept out of Miles's way. Susie was in a mood.

She had been for a walk with Dimitri and it was clear
that they had had a fight. Everything he said she contradicted loudly and flatly. And when she asked him to
drive her to the village, as Chris had put an embargo on
her driving the car herself, Dimitri said swiftly that he
was going water-skiing.

So that took care of the boat, Diana thought with an
inward sigh of relief. If Dimitri was using it to water-
ski, there was no possibility of Miles taking her out in
it for the sort of tête-à-tête he obviously had in mind.

Across the wooden table, Miles met her eyes and gave
her a slow smile. It was not reassuring.

Chris said, 'I'm sorry, Dimitri. Miles is using the boat
this afternoon.'

Miles said lazily, 'Don't worry. It can wait.'

Diana expelled a little breath she didn't even know she
had been holding. So her reprieve was confirmed.

But it wasn't.

'Diana wants to practise her swimming,' he continued
blandly and untruthfully, 'but I can just as well take her
to the little beach to the east. No one will disturb us
there.'

There was an odd silence. Looking round, Diana saw
that it was not just to her ears that it had sounded like
a command. She looked down at her plate, blushing
furiously.

Chris said, a shade too heartily, 'Susie, you'd better
tell Michalis to drive you.'

Miles nodded, as if satisfied. I'll kill him, thought
Diana, acutely embarrassed.

Susie's eyes were blank. Her heavy brows almost met.
She said to Miles, 'So I certainly shan't disturb you.'
There was an edge to it.

Once again, Diana recognised, she had been outman-
oeuvred. She balked at making a scene—especially since

she was sure that all the other participants would join in with enthusiasm. So she borrowed a bikini from the general cache, put her own shorts and shirt over it, and allowed Miles to lead her sedately down the rugged path to the east of the castle.

He met her with a large cartwheel hat, which he set on her head.

'Thank you,' she said between her teeth.

He was laughing. 'Better than frying your brains. I've brought your sun stuff too. Chris gave it to me. Was he oiling your back for you this morning?'

Diana disdained to answer that one. He laughed.

He took her hand again. She did not withdraw it. The ground was stony and her ankle would have turned too often without that support.

It was hot and the insects buzzed. The sparse bushes at the margin of the beach smelt like herbs in a kitchen— warm and aromatic. There were poppies among the long, waving grasses.

'It's beautiful,' Diana said involuntarily.

Miles looked round, then up at the castle, lowering over them like a Transylvanian fortress.

'But exposed. I've got a better idea,' he said. 'We'll go round the headland.'

Diana looked at it doubtfully. It looked pure granite.

'There's a path?' she asked.

'We swim,' he said succinctly.

She was alarmed. 'I couldn't. You know I don't really swim. I get in a panic if I can't put my feet on the bottom.'

'You won't with me,' Miles told her softly. 'Come on.'

And before she could say anything more he was running her into the little waves. The water struck cold and she spluttered. She was still spluttering when she felt him flip her on to her back and his hands came under her armpits.

'I'll tow you round,' he said in her ear. 'You can practise your swimming later.'

Diana was helpless. She turned her head in the water, glaring at him.

'I'll never forgive you for this.'

'Add it to the list.' Miles was not obviously repentant. 'Relax, for heaven's sake, I won't let you go. Trust me.'

'Great,' she said with irony. 'I've got real reasons to trust you, of course.'

'Don't start bitching mid-ocean,' Miles said comfortably. 'You can tell me what you think of me when we land. Much more satisfactory.'

He swam with lazy, powerful strokes that took them out of sight of the castle in minutes and had them landed in a small, almost enclosed bay almost as fast.

Diana gave a sigh of thankfulness as her feet touched the bottom. She stood up and waded out, looking around her. Her anger dissipated in sheer shock. It was beautiful, too, but it looked the loneliest place in the world. The beach was a great swath of white sand, bordered by tall rushes and overlooked by the sheer cliff.

She turned on Miles.

'Why have you brought me here? What are you doing?'

He gave her his old, lop-sided grin. He looked tough and capable and terrifyingly strong.

'Use your imagination,' he said softly.

She stared at him, mesmerised. The cotton of her soaked shirt plastered against her body in the faint breeze that came from the sea. Diana was oblivious. He came towards her. She closed her eyes. The hard brown hands were cool from the sea. The air hummed. He was quite slow and very gentle about it. But there was no way she was going to escape.

Diana screwed her eyes tight, tight shut so that red caverns danced before her inner vision. It was no use. His salty mouth closed hungrily on her own and her every sense opened to him.

CHAPTER SIX

IT WAS getting dark when they got back to the castle. The sun was only just visible above the distant hills and the moon was already high. The sea shifted and glimmered behind them, giving off little salty breaths of breeze.

The half-dark somehow made them seem much closer together. Closer and alone.

Diana climbed the cliff path without touching Miles. It was an effort she would not admit. She was shivering. This time there was no sun to dry off her clothes as soon as she emerged from the sea.

Miles said something under his breath. She ignored it. And when he offered her his hand over a difficult stretch she pretended she didn't see it. She was in turmoil.

There were lights in the kitchen and the corridors. But nobody was about. Presumably everyone had gathered on the battlements already. Diana was grateful. She knew she couldn't face anyone yet.

'I'm going to my room,' she told Miles, not looking at him.

He looked at her bent head.

'I take it that isn't an invitation,' he said drily.

Her head came up at that.

'As always, you are right,' she agreed, pushing a strand of damp, loosened hair back off her neck.

His mouth twisted. 'You look like a schoolgirl.'

Diana turned carefully, her eyes just missing his. 'Hardly a schoolgirl. As you've just demonstrated.' She kept her voice level with an effort. But the bitterness showed—bitterness and acute humiliation.

If I don't get away from him this minute, I'm going to start howling, thought Diana. She set her jaw grimly.

'I need a shower. I want to wash my hair before I present myself at dinner.'

Miles was not deceived. 'Going to ground, Di?' he challenged softly.

That did get her looking at him. Her grey-green eyes were glacial with hurt and indignation.

'Why should I do that?' she asked.

He touched her cheek. 'I can think of any number of reasons. None of which I like,' he said ruefully. 'Trying to pretend it didn't happen?'

Diana's eyes flashed. 'Happen? *Happen*? Like an act of God or something? Nothing happened that you didn't intend right from the start.'

'Are you so sure of that?' Miles asked quietly.

Her eyes hated him. 'You took me to a deserted beach. And jumped on me,' she said with precision. 'As you planned to do. Do you deny that?'

Miles winced. But he said mildly, 'I thought the jumping was mutual.'

Diana drew a sharp breath.

'Wasn't it?' he insisted.

He had more than a grain of right on his side. But Diana was too angry to be honest and too hurt to be fair.

'I don't recall being offered a choice,' she flung at him.

She turned away abruptly, afraid that the threatening tears were going to spill over. Tears of temper, she assured herself feverishly. Tears of temper.

'Di——'

But at the old name she whipped round. He was the only person who shortened her name, ever. It used to be a sign of affection. Suddenly she couldn't bear it.

'Don't call me that,' she said furiously. 'Don't ever call me that again.'

The handsome face registered no reaction whatsoever. But the piercing eyes narrowed, interested. Oh, lord, she had given herself away. She had shown too much.

She scrabbled for some sort of composure.

'I don't know what you think you're trying to do, Miles. Surely, we're both agreed, there's no future for us.'

The steep lids drooped, then lifted with startling suddenness, catching her nearly off-guard. Diana drew back.

'I don't remember discussing the future. Sometimes the present can be fun,' he drawled.

'Not for me,' she retorted. 'I'm not like that. You ought to remember that, at least.' For the first time since the beach she looked him in the eye. 'No one-night stands, Miles. Not for me.'

'Not with your husband?'

He was amused, Diana realised in outrage. He had torn her carefully constructed world to shreds with those long, clever fingers and he thought it was funny. Her rage suddenly went several notches deeper, and cooled to a cutting edge.

'That's a fiction,' she drawled in her turn. 'We both know it.' She saw his jaw tighten and felt a harsh, angry triumph. She went on, 'And before you remind me that your allowance pays my parents' mortgage you can forget it. From now on we won't take another penny.'

The brown eyes flickered and went absolutely impenetrable. 'I thought you couldn't afford it on your own.'

He sounded faintly interested. 'How are you going to explain it when they lose the roof over their heads?'

Diana swallowed. 'They'll understand,' she said desolately. 'They love me.'

That earned a fierce silence. She could feel his anger beating at her. She held herself very straight, braced in every nerve for his next move.

Miles didn't move. He didn't say anything either. His eyes flicked up an down her without noticeable expression.

She thought, He's trying to make me feel guilty. I won't. I won't. I won't let him play on my feelings the way he used to. She set her teeth.

At last he said softly, 'A gesture, Di? At any cost?'

She lifted her chin.

'You don't seem to understand, Miles. After today——' Her voice trembled. She steadied it with an immense effort and went on bravely, 'After today I want you out of my life completely. It's obvious we can't be friends...'

'And why do you think that is?'

She ignored him. '...as today's events have proved. So I don't want to have to see you, or hear about you, or think of you ever again.' She made a violent gesture which contrasted sharply with the level voice. It revealed all too clearly the strength of her feelings but she was beyond caring. 'Finish!'

Miles surveyed her. He pursed his mouth. 'Dramatic,' he commented.

For a moment Diana, who had never raised a hand in anger in her life, seriously considered hitting him. Miles took in her white face and the glittering intensity of the green eyes and seemed to sense that she was on a knife-edge of control. His voice gentled.

'We'll talk about it tomorrow.'

It was somehow the final insult, that gentleness. Diana took a spontaneous decision.

'No, we won't. I'm leaving tomorrow,' she flung at him. 'You've no hold over me and you can't keep me here.'

Miles considered that.

'Isn't running away rather pointless?' he asked.

She was so angry she could have screamed. Instead she gave him a fierce, mocking smile and said, 'I wouldn't know. You're the one who runs, Miles.'

She turned her back on him and started to go inside.

'*What*?'

He was in front of her suddenly, as quick as a panther—and as dangerous. All the careful negligence was gone. His eyes drilled into hers. Diana glared back, refusing to quail.

'*You* went,' she reminded him, her voice low and bitter. 'I didn't.'

He stared, his face fierce. 'You told me to.'

She pushed her drying hair back with hands that shook.

'Miles, you'd just said I'd got the wrong man if I wanted a father substitute,' she said, her voice raw. 'I was devastated. And then you thought I'd fall into your arms...' She shuddered, remembering. 'Yes, that night I was angry too, and I wanted to be left alone. That *night*, Miles. I didn't expect you to walk out on me forever. It was you who chose to do that. And, having chosen,' her voice was suddenly ragged, 'keep to it. Now get out of my way.'

He stood back without a word.

When she got to her room, she tore off her clothes as if they were infected. She would, she promised herself, burn the shorts and shirt. The borrowed bikini was a different matter. Even in her present rage, Diana recognised that she couldn't burn someone else's clothes.

She looked at herself in the mirror with dislike. The bikini was tiny and sophisticated in cut, brilliant in colour. Suddenly she saw what Miles had seen—her breasts half revealed by the jade stuff, artfully piped with black to emphasise the contours it covered. The tiny briefs laced round her pale hips, the lacings an evident invitation. She turned away, her mouth twisting with distaste. The whole garment was designed to be taken off by someone else—all the fastenings stood out, black and blatant.

Maybe Miles wasn't as much to blame as she thought. She should never have worn it.

She went into the bathroom and began the slow process of running a bath. As the steam began to rise, she untied the black strips from around her neck and scrambled out of the briefs. The bikini fell. Diana assiduously avoided her image in the mirrors with which the room was plentifully provided.

Her body felt different. She did not want to see the evidence. She wondered whether she would ever be comfortable looking at her own naked body again. Even alone in the privacy of her steamy bathroom she felt her colour rise at the thought.

This, she told herself grimly, was ridiculous. This was running away indeed. Deliberately, she turned to face a mirror. There were very faint marks on her thighs. The shadow of a bruise on her throat. Her breasts were tender. It could be the sun, she reminded herself. It had been burning hot and she had had no protection from it. Except Miles's body when—— She gave a little moan, seeing herself flush.

But it was the mouth that really gave her away, she thought, wincing. It looked swollen and vulnerable. You

might miss the shadows on her skin, but that mouth to[l]
its own tale.

She closed her eyes, ashamed to remember. Wh[a]
marks had she left on Miles? What had *happened*? The[y]
never treated each other like that in the old days.

And then it all came back in an unwelcome rush. Dian[a]
sat limply on the edge of the bath, wishing she didn[']
have to remember.

How long had Miles held her mouth in that first de[s]
perate kiss? A minute? Longer? Until he knew she w[as]
his, anyway. It had left Diana weak, startled as muc[h]
by her own response as his action. When he lifted h[is]
head, she couldn't look at him. Her breathing was swi[ft]
and shallow. He ran his palms down her arms, bare[ly]
touching the skin. Her breath caught, and she shivere[d]

Miles took her hands and carried first one and the[n]
the other to his lips. He just brushed a whisper acro[ss]
her knuckles; but the kiss he pressed into the palm w[as]
passionate.

Something clenched hard inside Diana. She felt as [if]
she was taking painful, dangerous steps up a critic[al]
staircase. It left her dizzy and afraid—and with no choic[e]
but to go on.

He tucked a straying wisp of the damp fair hair behi[nd]
her ear. He was very gentle then. He trailed his fingerti[p]
over her cheekbone, her nose, her chin. Diana's li[ps]
parted. He touched the finger to her lower lip. Dian[a]
gasped.

Behind them the ocean was almost silent. The bree[ze]
had dropped, leaving the air like warm honey. On th[e]
hill behind them birds twittered. There was a buzz [of]
insects and, far out in the bay, the distant chug of [a]
motor on the still air. They were utterly alone.

Miles traced her mouth with his thumb. He looke[d]
intent, absorbed. Oh, there had been times when sh[e]

thought she would drown in those warm, laughing eyes. Diana swayed towards him. It was another step up that perilous ladder.

Miles held her very lightly. His mouth drifted butterfly kisses over her face. Diana trembled and his hold tightened. But he didn't stop. She felt his tongue briefly against her temple and then, with infinite care, between her lips. She gave a long, long shudder and put her arms round him. Another step.

He picked her up then. Diana had forgotten how easily he could do it. It had always alarmed her. She would cry out, feeling insecure and half annoyed. This time was different. She felt languorous in his arms, utterly safe. But she knew he remembered her old trepidation because he laughed down at her—with something that was not laughter at all in the brown eyes.

Slowly, almost dreamily, she lifted one hand from his shoulder and ran it along the smooth brown jaw. Miles turned his head, so that her drifting fingers touched his mouth and kissed them.

That was when things changed. That was the moment when she leaped the rest of the staircase and didn't know where she'd reached—the moment she stepped on to the thunderbolt and was flung into the heavens.

They were kissing before Miles lowered her to the ground. They were both shaking with impatience. The scraps of clothing were torn away, flung behind them as they locked together in a need too great for tenderness. Diana's throat arched and she drew Miles to her like a vice, crying out. In the end she heard him cry out too.

'Oh, lord,' said Diana wearily now, drooping on the side of her bath.

They had ridden the thunderbolt, all right. Together. When the explosion came she had been clinging to him, sobbing, holding him with fierce love. Oh, Miles had had every right to say it was mutual.

It was total defeat. There was nothing she wouldn't have done, nothing she wouldn't have agreed to, with his head dropped against her breast. She had felt utterly peaceful.

Utterly—she said it to herself now deliberately—in love.

She put her fingers to her tender mouth. It was her own fault, of course. All those brave statements of independence, all that insistence that he couldn't hurt her any more—it was all a disguise to cover the fact that she had never, not for a moment, stopped loving him. Not when he was angry, not when he was cold, not on the evenings he went to Susie without a word of excuse or explanation, not even when he looked at her with that indifference that hurt worse than anything else.

She looked at him and she was hungry for his love. It was hopeless.

Wearily she got into the bath and closed off the taps. She lay back, trying to unknot her tense muscles. There must be something she could do. She had got over him before, she told herself desperately. Her brain went round and round. If she didn't see him again; if there was nothing left connecting them, not even the allowance; if she never saw his friends or went to places where he had been ... But there was no avoiding the truth. She was in love with the man and would be till the day she died.

'I've just got to take damned good care he doesn't find out,' she told herself out loud. 'If he doesn't know already, that is. Which, knowing Miles, he probably does.'

It was not a comforting thought. It drove her to dress carefully in one of her prettiest silvery green dresses and make up her face with care. It wasn't much of a suit of armour but it was something. And it had its effect.

A little silence fell when she joined the others on the lamp-lit battlements. Chris and Dimitri rose, staring at her. Miles was already on his feet in the shadows, his expression indecipherable.

Susie was an empress in scarlet and gold at the far end of the table. She greeted Diana warily, but her words were cheerful enough.

'Well, you don't look like a girl Miles dragged over sand and ocean half the day.'

Miles made a small movement, quickly stilled. He began to pour Diana a drink.

'You look very lovely,' he said slowly.

Susie said with an odd harshness, 'Did he make you swim till you dropped?'

Diana said carefully, 'I'm not a strong swimmer. But he got me there and back.'

Miles was giving her a glass of ouzo. The smell brought back older, sensuous memories. She gave a quick shiver, hurriedly repressed.

'Didn't I just?' he murmured, for her ear alone.

Diana pretended she didn't hear.

Christos said, 'Miles swims like a dolphin. He always has. But he's not very good at remembering that other people can be scared. I hope he didn't take you out of your depth, Diana?'

Miles stepped back, a small smile playing round his mouth. 'Did I?' he asked.

Diana glared at him. 'No.'

He gave a small nod. 'I thought not.' He sounded smug.

Susie said stiffly, 'Tomorrow you can take me climbing through rock pools and leave poor Diana to bask.'

Miles laughed softly. 'Tomorrow she's leaving.'

There was an outcry. Diana sat down and let it fly over her head. The others resumed their seats, arguing.

'Darling, *must* you?' wailed Susie.

'If you stay another three days, Dimitri can fly you back to London himself,' Chris said. 'If you're pressed for time that would save you a day's travelling at least. You've got room for a passenger, Dimitri?'

'With the greatest of pleasure.'

Miles frowned heavily. It was that really which decided her. She wanted to get away from him, true. But she also wanted to demonstrate how little she cared for him or his disapproval. She wanted quite desperately to do that. And if he didn't want her to fly with Dimitri— as he plainly didn't—here was the ideal opportunity.

'If you're sure . . .' she said hesitatingly.

Dimitri took her hand and kissed it.

'Positive,' he said caressingly.

Miles made a noise suspiciously like a snort. Diana felt a small glow of satisfaction.

'Then that's settled,' Chris said affably. 'Tomorrow Susie goes rockpooling with Miles and Diana basks.' He met Miles's look with amusement. 'And now we eat.'

In fact the next morning Diana was still so exhausted after one of the worst nights of her life that she did exactly what Chris foretold. She took her basket-weave chair under an olive tree out of sight of the windows and tried to concentrate on a popular novel. In the end she dozed off.

She woke to find Dimitri sitting at her feet, wearing a quizzical expression.

'Miles clearly wore you out yesterday,' he said drily.

Diana, well aware that he was fishing, managed not to blush.

'Swimming isn't my forte,' she told him calmly.

He laughed. 'So you said. So there wouldn't be much point in my asking you if you wanted to come out in the boat with me?'

'Not if I have to swim back,' she agreed. She stirred. The air was getting uncomfortably hot. There would be a breeze out on the bay. 'On the other hand, if all I had to do was to sit under a sunhat and watch *you* swim...'

Dimitri grinned. 'Deal. Come on, then, before Susie decides she and the rest of the world want to come too.'

There was an edge to his voice, Diana noticed. She went with him thoughtfully.

When he had had his swim and was back on board the gently rocking boat, she said carefully, 'Have you had a fight with Susie, Dimitri?'

He was stretched on the cover of the cockpit, exposing an already impressive tan. He kept his eyes closed but he made a face.

'You noticed?' he asked.

Diana said, 'Not really. I just wondered.'

He sighed, sitting up. 'She's being an absolute fool,' he said explosively. 'I have told her—but when did Susie ever listen to anyone else?'

'Except Miles,' Diana said quietly.

Dimitri gave a harsh laugh. 'Oh, she doesn't listen to Miles either normally. At the moment she's all sweet agreement because she thinks if she hangs on his every word he'll——' He stopped abruptly.

'He'll what?' Diana prompted, keeping her voice light. 'Fall in love with her? Marry her?'

Dimitri looked embarrassed. 'Lord knows.'

Well, it was more or less what she had worked out for herself. 'And will he?' she asked.

Dimitri was startled. 'You're better placed to answer that than I am, surely?'

She said evenly, 'I haven't seen Miles for two years until this week. I don't think I know him very well any more. If I ever did.' He gave her a look of considerable sympathy. More to herself than him she said, 'But I've never realised until...I suppose I always hoped, in the back of my mind somewhere, that we could try again. Have another chance. Stupid, of course, but fantasies usually are, aren't they?'

Dimitri looked at her soberly. 'Hope can be cruel,' he agreed.

She shook her head. 'Do you know—until yesterday I didn't even know I was still hoping?'

Dimitri came down from the cockpit roof and eased himself on to the deck beside her.

'Are you sure there really is no hope? I don't know Miles very well but, well, he clearly—er—cares for you.'

'He fancies me,' Diana corrected him brutally. It was like pressing on a bruise. She said it again with fury.

Dimitri was not shocked. He even looked a little amused. 'Who would not?' he said politely. 'But for Miles it is more than that, I think. And he is not happy.'

'If he isn't happy it's more likely to be his work—or even Susie—than anything to do with me. It always was.'

Dimitri nodded slowly. 'I see. But people change.'

'Not Miles,' Diana said with absolute conviction. She gave a little shiver, remembering his driven hunger on the beach. 'He wants me to do what he wants. He gets fighting mad when I don't. But he doesn't care whether or not I'm happy or bother about the things that interest me. He doesn't love me.'

'I see,' Dimitri said again. 'And this is why you were leaving so soon?'

'Yes. It must seem childish,' she admitted, 'but I was desperate to keep out of his way.'

Dimitri sighed. 'If it is childish then we both need to grow up. I too share this feeling.' He looked at her with a sudden flare of mischief lighting his sombre expression. 'Shall we run away together?'

Diana smiled. 'Where? Kathmandu? The ends of the universe?'

He shrugged. 'It would take that far to forget, I agree. But for today we could go just a little way.'

She stared. 'Are you serious?'

His smile faded. 'I'm serious about not wanting to sit down to lunch with Susie while she curls herself round Miles,' he said with suppressed violence.

Diana swallowed. 'Me too.' She touched his hand sympathetically.

'Right.' He stood up. 'That settles it. The Caves of Hippolytus. We'll go there for the afternoon. And we won't go home till dark.'

He started the outboard motor and turned the launch in a curving arc out of the bay.

Diana came to her feet unsteadily and went to stand beside him at the wheel. The salt spray in her face was not unpleasant.

'What are the Caves of Hippolytus?' she shouted above the noise of the engine.

Dimitri grinned. 'The stuff of adventure. Wait and see.'

It was quite a long journey. Out on the open sea, in the relatively sheltered gulf, the wind whipped the waves to a surprising height. The sun was still fierce but in the distance ominous purple clouds were massing on the horizon. She saw Dimitri glance at them a couple of times.

At last he cut the engine and guided the little boat carefully in between some rocks that stuck out of the water like icebergs. He moored them in the shelter of a sea cavern three times the height of a man.

'The Caves of Hippolytus,' he said, his voice echoing queerly.

Diana looked round. The waves slapping against the side of the boat also echoed in the rock dome.

'What are they?' she said in a whisper.

'Local legend says that Hippolytus was washed up here after his father had called up a wave to overturn his chariot and drown him,' Dimitri said. He was playing with the radio in the control panel. There was a quick sputter of Greek and he cut the connection. 'There. Now the coastguard know where we are. I've asked them to let the castle know. Just in case.'

Just in case Susie had missed him and was worried, Diana saw with compassion. Poor Dimitri. As long as Susie was with Miles, she wouldn't have any thoughts for anyone else.

He helped her out of the boat and around the shingly floor of the cavern. 'There's a whole network of caves,' he explained.

Diana looked round curiously. 'Inhabited?'

He shook his head. 'No. The tide comes up too high. Good for fishing, though. The caves are a sort of honeycomb of rock and water. There are quite big pools in there where you can't get a boat but you can get quite substantial fish.' He smiled. 'A couple of developers thought they could exploit the caves as a tourist trap. But they're too dangerous.'

'Dangerous?' Diana was surprised. She looked round at the calm cavern and the gently lulling sea beyond.

'Only at high tide, in bad weather, when you don't know what you're doing,' Dimitri told her fluently. 'You're safe with me.'

'Of course,' Diana said politely.

They scrambled through a tunnel into a bigger cave. It was weird, looking up through the spiral of rock to the sky. The clouds were moving quite fast now. When they got back to the main cavern, the water was slapping more agitatedly against the boat.

Dimitri looked at his watch. She knew he was going to say they ought to go. She suppressed the little lurch of the heart that told her she wasn't ready to go back and confront Miles.

Some piece of machinery on the boat began to beep. Diana jumped. Dimitri said, 'It's only the radio. I'll go and answer it. We should move soon anyway.'

'Let me have one last look round,' Diana pleaded.

He hesitated. But he clearly saw something in her face that swayed him. 'All right. Ten minutes,' he agreed.

And he waded out to the boat.

Diana turned and went down a tunnel they had not traversed before. She was glad of the moments alone. She liked Dimitri, but all afternoon she had been looking at him as if he were a ghost and Miles, the unseen, absent presence, was the real companion with her. It was not a pleasant feeling.

She wandered along the edge of another rock-locked pool and through a darker, damper tunnel. The floor sloped sharply and so did the ceiling. At times she was bent almost double. She had no torch so she couldn't see anything. But in the distance she heard water against rock and knew she would come out into another enclosed pool.

When she emerged it was as if it were a different day. The sky was gun-metal-grey and even in its shelter the water was violently agitated. The waves on the open sea were going to be quite something, Diana thought.

She squinted up. The rocks looked like granite: wet, sheer and deadly. High above her head there was a pinnacle like an angry finger stabbing at the sky. Well, if she got trapped there was no way out up the cliff-side, she thought wryly. Time to go back.

It was only as she tried to make her way back through the longest tunnel that she realised she wasn't going to be able to do it. The water was too high.

She felt a flutter of panic, but suppressed it. Dimitri knew where she was. She didn't think the caves were so extensive that he wouldn't be able to find her.

Eventually, said an inner voice. When the water goes down. And how high is it going to come first?

She went back to the pool. The water was definitely higher now. And it had begun to rain in great drops. Diana found the highest dry place she could locate and sat on the ledge, looking at the rising water. She was shaking, although it was hardly cold.

There was a brilliant flash and then she heard thunder in the distance. Rain fell harder. She brought her knees up to her chin and watched the pool below. She thought quite suddenly, I'm not going to get out of this.

She thought of Miles. Running away from him looked as if it was going to get her killed. He had been right, she thought with desperate irony. Running away never paid. If she ever had the chance, she would tell him.

Stop it, she said to herself. This is melodrama. You're not going to suffocate in the open air. You're not going to drown either. Bodies float and there's lots of stuff to hang on to, like the handrail in a swimming-pool. You're going to get wet and cold and miserable and it serves you right. But you're *not going to die.*

You can't afford to die. You've got to tell Miles you love him.

Diana jumped so hard that she nearly fell off her ledge. *Tell* Miles . . . ? What was she thinking of? But suddenly it seemed the most important thing in the world.

She dropped her head in her hands. If only she could see him once more; touch him . . .

She did not know how much time passed. The storm got nearer, bringing with it the strange illusion of human voices. Then, in a sudden lull, she realised there *were* voices. They were above her head. She looked up, astonished.

There were figures on the cliff. She couldn't make out who, through the driving rain. Except she had the crazy feeling they were fighting. She stood up, craning to wave. No one seemed to take any notice of her.

One of the figures detached itself and began to swarm up the pinnacle. Then he was standing on it, straight as an arrow, arms extended to a point above his head. He was going to dive into the enclosed pool.

A hand went to her throat. It must be incredibly fool-hardy. Even without the wind that was now whipping up the water, a dive from such a height into that heaving water would have been the height of recklessness.

In her head she heard Chris say, Our family have a taste for danger.

The man on the pinnacle seemed to fall in one graceful, uninterrupted arc. He cut into the black water as cleanly as a knife. As he plummeted, she saw the flash of copper hair. She backed against the wall of granite behind her and screamed aloud.

CHAPTER SEVEN

DIANA strained forward, agonised. Diving from that height, Miles must have gone right to the bottom. Was it deep enough? There must be a real risk that he would injure his head badly.

All thought of her own danger disappeared as she scanned the heavy sea below her. There was no sign of him. Diana began to rock backwards and forwards, her lips forming a silent prayer.

Please let him be all right. Please, I'll do anything. *Please*.

Then there was a splash. Diana stopped rocking, her eyes wide and tearless, fixed on the water. Another splash. Then a regular series of them. A smooth head appeared among the rhythmic spray. Miles powered towards her with fast strokes that sent the foam flying.

Diana went to the edge of her ledge. He trod water beneath her, shaking the water out of his eyes. His head and shoulders streamed. The copper hair was nearly black with water. He rubbed a powerful hand across his face to clear his vision, and Diana saw that his eyes were dark and sharp as daggers.

'What the hell,' he said, not attempting to disguise his temper, 'do you think you're doing?' He was breathing hard.

Diana didn't answer. She was too busy reaching a hand down to him. He barely touched it, hauling himself up the side of the chimney easily enough. Safe on the ledge, he turned to her.

'You have no *sense* sometimes,' he said furiously. He pulled her against him roughly. She was shaking with cold and the aftermath of fear. He cursed when he felt the tremors that shook her.

'Didn't you know it was dangerous? Wandering off like a four-year-old at a picnic.'

'I know,' said Diana, huddled against him, her lips against the cold, soaked skin of his shoulder. 'I know. I didn't think.'

'So you damned well should have.' Miles was looking rapidly round her eyrie, assessing the place. 'Not much shelter here.' He hesitated. 'Have you tried climbing?'

Diana raised her head and looked at the rock wall behind them. In his arms her trembling had quieted. Now her expression was rueful.

'There's a limit to how far I can climb,' she said. 'This is it.'

'They'll be back with a rope in half an hour or so,' he said, half to himself. He looked down at her assessingly. 'Very cold?'

She nodded. She was still held against the comforting strength of his body and she was not at all anxious to let him go.

'Not up to swimming?' he asked.

She looked down at the surging water, thought of the black tunnel, and shuddered. Miles detached her clinging hands and set her gently back against the rock-face. He surveyed their position narrow-eyed.

She started shivering again. Her finger-ends, she noticed with faint interest, were turning blue. In contrast—and in spite of his soaking—Miles looked warm and alive. He hunkered down in front of her.

'Look, Di, I know it goes against the grain, but you'll have to trust me.'

She looked at him blankly. He sighed as if he was trying to curb impatience.

'I can get you out of here,' he told her clearly. 'If you trust me. I can tow you through the cave in a life-saving hold.' His eyes gleamed briefly. 'The way I got you out to the beach. There's still air in the corridor. It will take ten minutes at the outside. Maybe less. But we'll both be at risk if you panic or try to fight me.' He took her icy hands. 'Will you trust me?'

Diana looked at the turbulent sea below them. There was no one on the headland above them now. They would have gone for help as Miles said. The storm clouds were racing and the wind was very cold.

She tried to force her icy lips to smile. 'There's n-not a lot going for us here,' she agreed. 'I'll have to.'

His eyes flickered. But his only response was to aim a playful fist at her cheek in a mock punch. 'That's my girl.' He took her hand, pulling her upright. 'Come on.'

'N-now?'

'Nothing to be gained by waiting,' Miles said in a practical tone. 'I'd take your skirt off. It won't be nice waterlogged and it could get in my way.'

It was a dress. Diana hesitated only momentarily. His gaze was almost clinical as he held out his hand for the scrap of cloth. He dropped it casually behind him.

'It'll be safe. We can collect it at low tide if you're specially fond of it.' He slipped off the ledge into the surging water. Bracing himself one-handed against the rock-face, he held the other up to her. 'Come on.'

The water was worse than before, boisterous as well as cold. Her feet touched the bottom and she staggered, sinking. She bit her lip till the blood ran, grabbing for him instinctively. His hands were as steady as hawsers.

'Don't think,' he instructed unemotionally. 'Let yourself float. Relax.'

It wasn't the easiest instruction in the world to comply with, Diana thought, amused in spite of her alarm. The water bumped her against him uncontrollably. Her own lack of ease in the water didn't make it any easier. But in the end he had her floating on her back, held against his chest.

Looking over his shoulder, he took them with steady strokes towards the rock passage. They seemed, to Diana's fluttering senses, to cover the distance in half a dozen sweeps of one powerful arm. As they plunged into darkness she gave an instinctive gasp that she wasn't quick enough to suppress. At once the arm that held her tightened.

'Don't think,' Miles said calmly. 'Relax.'

He kept on saying it as they swam and bumped their way through the little passage. The water was very high and it seemed to Diana that they were in imminent danger of scraping their faces on the roof.

Once she felt Miles hit the rock wall and flinch, swearing. But he was right. It didn't take much over ten minutes.

Dimitri was waiting in the boat. He wasn't alone. Chris was there, looking surprisingly grim. So were a couple of strangers who turned out to be fishermen.

They hauled her on to the launch and plied her with rough towels, rougher brandy and fishy-smelling sweaters. Dimitri was conspicuously silent while Chris gave crisp instructions into the radio. No one, Diana saw from her huddle in the cabin, seemed to be paying much attention to Miles.

She tried to say as much. After all, he was cold too and probably twice as exhausted, even though he wouldn't have been as scared. She looked across at him, pulling his own shirt over his damp shoulders. He looked brisk and, she thought, taking in the tense jawline and hard profile, angry. The words died on her lips. Thunder started in the distance.

The boat came to land on a small beach. Chris's limousine was waiting, though for once his driver wasn't in immaculate uniform. She gave him a faint smile as the man came forward anxiously to help her. She got up the beach under her own steam, though.

She hesitated before getting into the car. It seemed sacrilege somehow—the pristine ivory leather seats and her tarred and fishy garments. Miles came up the beach at a run.

'Get in,' he said sharply.

It was beginning to rain again, great drops like coins that spattered on the Mercedes's bonnet and were converted into steam. Diana did as she was told. She held open the door for him too but he had already turned away. She sank back.

Dimitri crunched up the shale towards her. He leaned on the door, bending to make out her expression.

'You are all right? Truly?' he asked.

Diana nodded. A great weariness was beginning to settle over her. Dimitri looked down to the beach to the others.

'Miles is astonishing,' he said in an odd voice. 'I had no idea he could be so——' he hesitated '—dramatic.'

Diana gave a little laugh that broke in the middle.

'Neither did I.'

'No,' Dimitri agreed. He swung into the back of the car beside her. 'He has surprised all of us, I think.'

Miles finished his consultation with Chris and ran lightly back up the beach to the car.

'The castle,' he said to the chauffeur. 'The Count will take the boat back.'

He got in and the car rocked gently up the unmade track. Miles looked round at her.

'You're cold and a bit shocked but I think that's all. We'll have a doctor look at you but I don't think we need to run you into the clinic as an emergency. Do you?'

Diana shook her head violently. 'Of course not. I was just stupid. It was you...' She remembered that brush with the rock wall and winced.

'I'm OK,' he said curtly.

Dimitri said, 'I've never seen a dive like that. Have you always dived?'

They began to discuss the local swimming. Diana's head spun. The car was warm and superbly sprung. She began to droop sideways.

She awoke to find herself being carried. She thought she was being pulled out of the car. 'Dimitri?' she said, still three-quarters asleep.

'No,' said Miles grimly. 'Think again.'

She was long out of the car. He was taking her down the corridor in the castle. He shouldered open the door to her room. Diana's eyes focused with difficulty.

Miles dropped her on the lace-covered bed and began to strip off the odorous sweaters. Her cold fingers closed over his own, trying to stop him.

The sherry-brown eyes glinted down at her. 'Quite apart from the fact that we've been married for years, if you believe you came out of the sea anything other than effectively naked, you're living in fairyland,' he told her brutally.

She flushed, turning her face away, hating him again.

Miles took no notice. He peeled off the jerseys with his customary efficiency, ridding her of the scraps of despised underwear. He flung a robe at her.

'Put that on. I'll run you a bath.'

She huddled into it, glaring at his back. Protest was clearly going to be useless. He slammed the bathroom door.

Diana rubbed the shivering flesh on her arms. She couldn't remember Miles like this, she thought. Oh, he'd been angry before, but never with this glittering danger as if at any moment he might lash out. He was always so cool, so remote. The sense that he might be at the edge of his control was almost frightening. Diana examined her feelings. No, not frightening—exciting.

Miles came out of the bathroom. The front of his shirt was damp again, revealing the muscles that had held Diana so securely. The dark red hair was curling uncontrollably after its soaking. Diana's mouth went dry. Miles bent and picked her up again, though she protested.

The bath was steaming. He slipped the robe off her shoulders and held her hand while she got in, then trickled water down her back out of a big sponge. Almost at once she felt the shattering cold along her spine begin to melt. His touch was quite impersonal, but Diana didn't feel impersonal at all. That was exciting too. She tipped her head back, closing her eyes, and gave herself up to the luxurious sensation of his hands on her again.

He said nothing, playing the warm water over her steadily.

After a while Diana opened her eyes and tried to behave sensibly. She said with a little difficulty, 'I can do that. I'm all right now. Shouldn't you have a bath yourself? You got as cold as I did.'

She met his eyes. They gleamed. He didn't look impersonal after all.

'Are you inviting me to join you?' he asked.

Heat flooded her cheeks and she sat up straighter. 'No,' she choked, though her flesh trembled at the thought. Could he see that? She turned her head away, furious with herself. And ashamed.

'Only in salt water?' Miles laughed down at her. 'Cold salt water? You may have a point.' But he handed her the sponge, searching her flushed face. 'You're sure you're all right?'

She nodded, still conscious of that burning blush. His hands left her without apparent reluctance.

'Then get into bed when you're finished,' he said practically. 'I'll have a hot drink sent up. You probably need food too.'

She shook her head. Miles took no notice.

'Don't fall asleep in the bath either,' he instructed. 'I'll be back to make sure.'

His last threat had Diana out of the water and huddled in a nightshirt under the bedcovers in five minutes flat. Which was just as well because, true to his word, he was back in less than ten. He brought a tray of food.

Diana looked at it with loathing, hugging her arms round her knees.

'I don't want anything to eat,' she said militantly. 'I told you so.'

Miles slanted a look down at her. 'Maybe not. But it stops anyone else thinking you do and bringing it up.'

Diana stared.

'I can do without any further interruptions,' he explained, putting the tray down on a distant table.

Diana's mouth went dry again. 'Why?' she said to his back. It came out as a croak. She cleared her throat and tried again. 'Why?'

He turned back to her. His smile was wry.

'There are too many people around. Haven't you noticed? When I arranged to get you here I hadn't bargained on a damned houseparty.'

His eyes were very bright. They searched her face as if they saw secrets there that not even she was aware of.

Diana felt that treacherous excitement begin to burn again. She could not tear her eyes away from his.

'Wh-what do you mean?'

'Whenever I look for you, you're with somebody else. Whenever I get you alone, someone interrupts.'

Except on the beach. Neither of them said it, though Diana's cheeks were suddenly on fire. His expression was rueful.

'Or I get you alone and we don't talk,' he agreed. 'Don't you think we need to talk, Di?'

She moved restlessly. 'You were never very good at talking as far as I remember,' she muttered.

He grimaced. 'Guilty as charged,' he said, to her surprise. 'Those last weeks I was hell to live with, I know. I'd let work get out of hand and...'

'Not just weeks,' Diana said without thinking. 'And not just work.'

'...I didn't know what to do about us. *What* did you say?'

He looked so startled that she felt the easy colour rise again.

She would have given anything to recall her betraying words. But it was too late. She would have to admit to his face what he must already know, Diana thought resentfully: that she had never understood the hold Susie had over his affections and had been bitterly intimidated by the other woman's glamour and sophistication.

She lifted her chin and met his eyes defiantly.

'It had been going wrong for months and you know it.'

Miles's eyes were shrewd. 'And?'

Diana swallowed but her chin went higher.

'And when you didn't come home at night you weren't always in the Physics building,' she flung at him.

His face went absolutely still. She had the feeling that behind the mask the clever brain was racing. But his expression gave no sign of it. As usual, she thought bitterly.

'Did you think I was unfaithful, then?' he asked at last softly. 'Out on the town? Cheating on you?'

To Diana's wincing ears it sounded almost like a taunt. She flung her hair back and met his eyes proudly.

'I thought it was probable, yes,' she told him in a level voice.

The brown eyes flickered.

'Who with, for heaven's sake? I was spending all my waking hours with a computer and Steve Gilman.'

'Not,' said Diana with precision, 'all.'

Miles gave a sharp exclamation, abruptly cut off. His eyes burned into hers. She met the look unflinchingly. She was not, after all these months dealing with life on her own, going to let him intimidate her, she thought with determination.

At last he expelled a long breath. 'I see. Whatever happened to trust?' His voice was bitter.

Diana said quietly, 'Trust has to be earned.'

He winced. 'You thought I'd let you down? Lied to you?' He sounded incredulous.

She hesitated. Had she ever thought Miles was lying? He kept his own counsel and he never explained what he was doing or why. But lying?

'Not exactly,' she said.

'Then what are you talking about?'

She found she was twisting her hands together. It was an old sign of agitation, and Miles would recognise it as such. She stilled them.

'Well, you didn't exactly tell me the whole truth about your life, did you?' she said. 'I didn't know about your father, for example. Or that you owned this house. Or that Chris and Susie were your cousins, not just friends.'

He was watching her with a curious expression. 'All that stuff was important?'

She shook her head vigorously. 'No. Don't you see, Miles? If you'd told me it wouldn't have mattered a row of beans. What mattered was that there were big bits of your life that you didn't want me to know about. Secrets, Miles. They're not good for mutual trust.'

He said softly, 'But these are all things you've found out in the last week. They weren't the reason we broke up.'

Diana shut her eyes. 'We broke up,' she said with an effort, 'because we didn't have a marriage any more.'

There was a long, sizzling silence.

Then Miles said, 'Didn't we? How did you come to that conclusion?'

Diana opened her eyes and found he was strolling towards the bed. Like a stalking jaguar, she thought, with a little rush of alarm.

She said hurriedly, 'Look, Miles. You worked. We hardly spoke. Not for weeks. For over a year. And then when Susie rang you—you dropped everything and went to London to see her.'

He stopped as if she had felled him.

'Susie?' he echoed softly.

There was an expression in his eyes that made her heart flutter frantically. She went on, almost gabbling, 'Of course you were fond of her. I knew that. And you knew her better than you knew me. She's more your sort of person. She's got the same background. I could see that even before I knew you were cousins. But you didn't say why she needed to see you or when you'd be back—or if you were coming back——'

'Susie,' he said again on a long breath.

He gave no sign of having heard a word she'd said, Diana thought. She pleated the edge of the coverlet with fingers that trembled imperceptibly.

'You thought I was having an affair with *Susie*.' It was an accusation.

She glared at him, in spite of her tremors.

'It seemed a reasonable deduction.'

'Did it?' Miles was grim. 'Why didn't you ask me, for heaven's sake?'

'I thought I did.' She winced, remembering the stilted conversations, Miles's harsh, impatient answers. 'You didn't seem to be making a secret of it.'

He passed a hand over his face. 'Dear heaven,' he said wearily. 'I didn't realise. It never occurred to me. What made you think of Susie?'

Diana looked down. She could, of course, have told the literal truth and said, She did. But it wasn't the whole truth, and somehow she didn't feel that less than the whole truth would do.

So she said carefully, 'You were obviously close. And she's gorgeous. And everyone else seemed to expect you'd marry her if you married anyone.'

He shook his head, wordlessly.

'And even when you weren't talking to me you went to her whenever she called,' Diana finished simply.

'I—oh, lord, yes, I suppose I did,' Miles said as if it was wrenched out of him. 'And I suppose from your point of view I'm still doing it, aren't I?'

Diana flinched.

He said urgently, 'Look, I'll get rid of her. I'll get rid of them all. We'll be alone with some time to ourselves. We'll just take it as it comes.'

She shut her eyes. Being alone with Miles with time to themselves would, she thought, just about take out all her defences. Could she afford it?

As if he sensed her inner turmoil, he said carefully, 'No promises. No pressure. Just a holiday we both need. After all, we always got on well enough, didn't we?'

She could have screamed that once he had withdrawn into himself they had not got on at all. And her every day had been a nightmare—to say nothing of the empty nights. But she was shaking with reaction already. She didn't think she could take a full-scale confrontation about his personal isolation.

So instead she said carefully in her turn, 'It's difficult to get on badly with someone who may just have saved your life.'

He made an abrupt, dismissive gesture. 'Will you stay with me, Di?' His voice was low.

Her defences were pretty flimsy things after all.

'Yes,' she said.

CHAPTER EIGHT

SLIGHTLY to Diana's surprise, Miles wasn't triumphant at his easy victory. Nor did he attempt to take immediate advantage of it.

Instead he touched her cheek very lightly with the back of his hand.

'Sleep,' he said. 'You need it. You look like a ghost. We'll talk later.'

He went noiselessly from the room without waiting for an answer. Which was just as well, Diana thought wryly, because she hadn't the faintest idea what she would have said to him. He seemed to have her in the palm of his hand again.

She sank back among the pillows, disturbed. Oh, she knew it all, the faint tremors that radiated out from the spine through her whole body, the hunger for his touch, the fear... She screwed her eyes tight shut. That was the awful thing: the fear that he would turn away again, with his remote, polite smile, and remove himself into the far distance.

'I couldn't take that again,' Diana said aloud.

She turned her head into the pillow, shaken. Take it *again*? What was she thinking of? Dropping her independence like an old pair of jeans she had no further use for, and going back to Miles? Even if he wanted her—and he hadn't said he wanted her—that would be foolhardy in the extreme. Surely she wasn't going to let her heart run away with her again?

She fell asleep telling herself she would not be such a fool.

She didn't know what it was that brought her awake. She had been dreaming, some sad, familiar stuff where she huddled, shivering in a darkened doorway, waiting and afraid. When she awoke, she was still entangled in the webs of the dream, bewildered and desolate.

At first she didn't know where she was. She lifted her head and looked round, rubbing the back of her hand across her eyes like a child. Her face, she found, was damp with tears from the dream. The strange shapes of unknown furniture startled her. She sat up.

'Did I disturb you?' said a soft voice from the window.

Diana gave a small silent scream, her heart jumping. She swung over to look in the direction of the voice.

Out of the grey and lilac shadows, Miles strolled. He was like a shadow himself. She could not see his face, only the lithe, beautiful shape of his body and the characteristic tilt of his head. Her blood seemed to stop, then suddenly to start thundering at a new and audible rate.

She said his name. It was a voiceless whisper.

'Yes.'

She could tell from his voice that he was smiling. She shut her eyes, reaching for her common sense, her resolve, her sense of self-preservation.

'You shouldn't be here,' she said.

'An interesting proposition.' The husky voice was amused. Amused and determined. 'Why not?'

There was a soft rustle of cloth. Diana's eyes flew open. But she already knew what she would see. He was shrugging himself out of the pale shirt. It dropped unheeded. Oh, the times she had watched him do that! The times she had picked up the misused shirt the next day, holding it against her face, remembering their laughter and the crazy passion they incited in each other.

Diana scrambled up among the bedclothes with a small moan of panic.

'*No*,' she said, pushing the pillows away in an attempt to get off the bed and on to her feet.

But Miles turned neatly and took her by the shoulders, hauling her across the bed to where he stood at its head. In the cool shadows, his hands were like fire. She shuddered with a feeling she would infinitely have preferred not to recognise. There was no doubt that Miles recognised it. He laughed softly as she put her hands against his chest, trying to lever herself away from him.

He kissed her. Her protest shuddered into silence.

The terrifying thing, Diana thought muzzily, was that it was all so *familiar*. It was nothing like those crazy, calculated minutes on the beach. This was what she knew, what she had grown used to—the absolute physical rapport, a refinement of sensation so exquisite that it was almost a pain.

In all the bleak days of her independence she had never once looked for another lover. And here he was, proving again, unequivocally and unforgettably, exactly why. It would have been pointless. Only Miles had ever made her feel like this, Diana thought. Only Miles ever could.

If he leaves me again, I'll die, she thought. She had just enough presence of mind not to say it aloud.

Their clothes fell in their accustomed tangle. Their bodies moulded into the accustomed attitudes. There was, perhaps, a new intensity. He did, perhaps, hold her more fiercely as she ran her lips over his skin. Diana heard him catch his breath. His throat arched. She was trembling wildly, out of control. She gave herself up to the feelings that swept them both into the whirlwind.

The next time she awoke, she was smiling. She turned lazily, filled with a sense of sunshine and well-being that she had not had for months.

The shutters were open. The Attic sun streamed in like wine, blasting colour out of the elaborate hangings. Diana stretched like a cat, looking at the room through half-closed eyes. It was a ridiculous room for a climate like this, she thought. She must make Miles get rid of these tapestries and weighty furniture.

She turned towards him, reaching out a hand for the support of his shoulder. But she was alone.

It disconcerted her. She sat up, her eyes flying open. Perhaps he was in the bathroom?

But no. The bathroom door was open and no sounds came from it. A chill touched her. She pulled the coverlet up to cover her breasts, scanning the room for clues that he had been there, that it had not all been a dream.

There was nothing. The tangle of masculine clothes had gone from the rug beside the bed. Her own cotton nightdress had been draped modestly over the end of the bed. Apart from that, you wouldn't think Miles had been there at all.

All Diana's doubts surged back like an unwelcome revelation. Had he said he loved her last night? Had he said anything at all last night? He had said her name on that shaken little note of laughter and passion which had delivered up her soul to him. But of his thoughts, his own feelings, he had said nothing. He had kept his own counsel. Just, Diana reminded herself, growing colder by the minute, as he used to.

She scrambled off the bed, pulling the coverlet self-consciously round her. But there was no one else in the suite. She put her head out of the door: no one else in the corridor. There was no one on the terrace either. And nothing that could be construed as a message.

Diana dressed swiftly and went looking.

She found Christos Galatas on the battlements. There was no sign of anyone else, though the sun was so high that it had to be mid-morning. Christos was looking pre-occupied and not very pleased.

'Miles has gone,' he said tersely.

Diana stopped as if he had hit her.

'Gone?'

He looked at her narrowly. 'I was going to ask you if you knew. But obviously you didn't.'

She put out a hand and lowered herself into a seat blindly. She felt numb.

Again. He had left her again. Without a word, or a kiss or so much as a note to say where he was going. I don't believe it, she thought. But then, at a deeper, harder level, Yes, I do.

And yet, after last night, how could he? She would have sworn that he was as moved as she was. Even though he hadn't put it into words, she knew how he had trembled under her hands. Surely that meant something? *Surely*?

Nothing, Diana thought, was ever going to hurt her again as much as this second desertion.

Chris was speaking. '. . . taken my damn fool sister with him.'

She drew a sharp little breath. Wrong again; something could hurt worse. She gave a sudden, harsh laugh. She'd thought if Miles left her again she would die. Well, this was where she found out how you went on living with a second mortal wound.

Chris looked at her for a narrow-eyed moment. 'Has he gone to write his Russian paper?' he asked.

Diana winced. But she said coolly enough, 'I have no idea why he's gone. Or where.'

'He didn't tell you?'

She shook her head. 'Miles never told me much when I was married to him. Now. . .' She shrugged.

'He seems to think you're still married to him.'

The pain round her heart was so bad that she felt as if the life blood was being squeezed out of it.

'Not,' she said grimly, 'for long.'

To his evident consternation, she insisted on leaving that day. He wanted Dimitri to fly her back to London but the other guest was nowhere to be found, so Chris abandoned that. He would not, however, hear of her driving the hired car back to Athens.

'You're upset,' he said flatly. 'You'll have an accident.'

'I am not upset,' Diana said.

She had packed with murderous speed. She was now holding on to her temper with the greatest of difficulty. She had to keep reminding herself that Chris was not responsible for his cousin's careless seductions.

'I've had a wonderful holiday,' she said with vicious politeness, 'and now I need to go back and get on with my life.'

'Miles will kill me,' he said gloomily.

But he ordered the chauffeured limousine to take her to the airport. He even accompanied her.

'What are you going to do when you get back?' he asked as they came into the Athenian suburbs.

'Work,' she said. 'Put my affairs in order. Get a divorce.'

He bit his lip and said nothing for a moment. Then, 'Why did you marry Miles, Diana?'

She drew a careful breath. She had asked herself that too in the last few hours. She knew the answer and there was no point in dissembling, furious though it undoubtedly made her.

'Because I was in love,' she said crisply. 'And Miles was so sure it was the right thing.' She shrugged. 'We seemed to fit. Then.'

Christos nodded. 'And Miles was in love,' he supplied.

Diana swallowed and set her jaw, looking out into the dusty streets.

'No,' she said. 'I very much doubt it.'

Chris sighed. 'Then you're wrong,' he said at last. 'Miles was so in love that it showed. Frankly, I envied him.'

He paused. She said nothing. He sighed again. He did not mention the subject again.

Diana hardly noticed the flight home. It was late and crowded and not all the Count's influence had succeeded in locating a first-class seat on a tourist-class flight. She was wedged into the window seat that his influence did manage to procure, flanked by a worried mother and a restless nine-year-old whose interest in herself didn't diminish until she was climbing into a taxi outside Heathrow.

Her little house was cold and dusty. Diana went round putting on lights and radiators. After the brightness of Greece it seemed cramped and dark.

Stop it, she told herself. This is the home you made for yourself when Miles left you. It's what you want. You're comfortable here. You're safe.

Ah, but am I happy? Will I ever be happy again?

Self-pity, she told herself grimly, will get you nowhere.

She went through her post like a whirlwind. When she had answered everything, she ran through the messages on the answering machine. Nothing from Miles, of course. Everything else was easily dealt with. Too easily. It was early afternoon and she had nothing to do to take her mind off the confused and painful thoughts that were churning away at the back of her mind.

She walked round the house with an undrunk mug of coffee in her hand, formulating plans and discarding them as soon as she thought of them. She went to put music on the stereo and her hand fell on the Bach English

Suites. Miles's favourites. She stuffed them back into the rack and played Charlie Parker loudly and defiantly.

When her thinking took her nowhere, she went looking for something stronger than coffee. There were the eight-week-old remains of a bottle of Sancerre in the fridge. She threw it away with a grimace and investigated the drinks cupboard. She drank so rarely that she couldn't remember what was there. She looked at the array of bottles with distaste: gin too sweet, brandy too dry, whisky was only for cold weather, ouzo...

She stopped dead. She had no idea how it had come there. She wouldn't have bought it and she couldn't have brought Miles's bottle from the marital home when she moved her things. Surely she couldn't.

'It's a conspiracy,' Diana said, shaking with fury.

With shaking fingers she took the bottle out of the cupboard and marched it into the kitchen like a prisoner under guard. There she twisted the top off viciously and flung the stuff down the sink. The warm smell of aniseed rebounded on her. She set her teeth, flinging the empty bottle into the swing-bin so hard that she heard it shatter.

'I will get him out of my life,' she vowed. 'I will be free. I *will*.'

Without thinking further she picked up the phone and dialled her lawyer. Joan was an old friend who had helped her set up her consultancy.

'Joan,' she said as soon as she'd identified herself, 'I'm divorcing Miles.' For some stupid reason the tears began to seep out of her eyes. She stuffed the back of her hand in her mouth to stop herself whimpering. She mastered her voice. 'Will you act for me?'

'Are you sure that's what you want?' Joan Dryden asked cautiously after a startled pause. 'Do you want to talk about this?'

'No,' Diana said curtly. 'I just want it over with as soon as possible.'

There was another pause. 'Er—well, that will depend on Miles as well, of course,' Joan ventured.

Diana gave a laugh that didn't—quite—break.

'I've seen Miles. He's got no grounds to contest a divorce.' She swallowed something huge and jagged in her throat. 'He's left me twice now.'

'Well, he's off lecturing, that's his job. You have to be reasonable,' Joan said with infuriating calm.

'He's off with Susanna Galatas,' Diana said coldly.

'Oh, lord,' said Joan, suddenly less the lawyer than the concerned friend. 'Oh, Diana, I'm so sorry. What a bastard.'

I will not cry, Diana told herself. She swallowed again.

'He was always close to her,' she said, her voice a model of indifference. 'He may even marry her. I don't care. I just want shot of him, Joan.'

'I don't blame you. I'll start drafting,' her friend said. 'Are you all right? I mean do you want me to come over or anything?'

'No. I'm going to see my parents,' Diana said on another of her instantaneous decisions. Her voice suddenly thickened. 'But thanks, Joan.'

She prepared more carefully for her visit to her parents the next day. If Miles was serious about his threat to stop her allowance, she would have to see if there was any way that between them they could carry on paying the mortgage. And she didn't want them to detect her own devastation. Not least because she didn't want to admit it herself.

They were delighted to see her. Her father was cooking in his skilfully adapted kitchen. He sent her out to talk to her mother, who was gardening.

Constance Silk hugged her, then held her a little away from her.

'Did you have a good holiday?' she said, searching her face. 'You don't look very brown.'

'Mum, I saw Miles,' Diana blurted, breaching all her prepared resolutions.

Mrs Silk sat down on a wooden bench that circled a pear tree and placed her trug under it. She was heart-breakingly unalarmed.

'Did you, now? I'm glad.'

Diana subsided beside her and took hold of herself rapidly. 'Don't be.'

Her mother looked faintly amused. 'Did you have another fight?'

One of the most difficult things to deal with since Miles had walked out had been, in Diana's experience, her mother's bland determination that it was a temporary interlude, resulting from Diana's losing her temper with a busy man she didn't appreciate.

Diana closed her eyes briefly. 'Mother, Miles and I fought all the time.'

Mrs Silk shook her head at her. 'You're the most contrary girl. You and Miles head over heels as you are, I'd have thought you could find something better to do than quarrelling.' And, having delivered her considered view, which Diana knew would not be repeated, she sat back and said comfortably, 'Now tell me how Miles is.'

Diana straightened her shoulders. She shielded her father a good deal but experience had taught her there was not much point in trying to hide things from her mother.

'Miles is getting tired of paying my allowance,' she said. 'We're going to have to look at the mortgage again. I'm not sure I can keep it up. Or not for long. I'm sorry.'

She waited for an outbreak of emotion. None came.

'You must have made him very angry this time,' Constance Silk said thoughtfully.

Diana decided to tell her everything. Or at least all the facts. The emotions she couldn't handle herself yet. She certainly wasn't going to try and explain them to someone else.

'I told him I didn't want to have anything more to do with him,' she said with a hint of defiance.

'Ah. I see now,' her mother said at length.

Diana stared. This was superhuman self-control.

'See what, Mum?'

'The solicitors in Oxford sent someone over last week. Wednesday, was it? Thursday? He said Miles thought the present arrangement was unsatisfactory. So he was going to pay off the mortgage entirely. Dad and I had to sign some papers. I thought,' said Constance Silk with the confidence of a woman who never bothered her head with such things, 'it was probably something to do with tax.'

'Pay off...?' A terrible fear took hold of Diana. 'You mean the house is in his name now?'

Mrs Silk looked shocked. 'Oh, I don't think so, dear. You'll have to ask your father. The solicitor brought the deeds back. Dad and I went into town and put them in the bank. It made a nice trip for him.'

Diana felt as if she had taken a step into quicksand. 'I don't understand.'

Mrs Silk sent her a shrewd look. 'I suppose Miles didn't want Dad and me to be mixed up in whatever fight you're having now,' she said comfortably. 'Very sensible of him.'

There was a shriek of triumph from the kitchen. Constance Silk stood up, looking pleased.

'Devil's Food Cake,' she said. 'It's a recipe he got out of a magazine. If you tell him you're on a diet I'll never speak to you again. Anyway, you look as if you could do with some more flesh on your bones. No one would think you've had a holiday.'

In the kitchen Frank Silk was swinging the wheelchair deftly from one counter-top to the other. His face was red, as much with pleasure as with the heat from the oven. On the baking tray stood a rich-looking chocolate cake. Diana looked at it with real admiration, repressing sternly the tears that pricked at her eyes.

'When can we start it?' she asked.

'I'll make tea now,' said her mother. 'It'll be cool enough by the time the kettle's boiled. Go and sit in the fresh air and I'll bring it out into the garden.'

Frank buzzed the wheelchair briskly down the specially constructed path and swung round to a stop under the pear tree. Diana dropped to the ground beside him. He looked down at her fondly.

'So you had a lovely holiday with Miles,' he said. He and Constance managed to communicate telepathically, Diana thought sourly. 'How is he?'

Her father had been shocked and angry when Miles left her. He seemed to have got over it now.

Diana said carefully, 'Fit. Very tanned.'

Frank nodded. 'Good. The last time we saw him he was looking like a ghost, I thought. Working too hard.'

'Yes,' said Diana automatically. She was trying to assimilate this piece of surprising news. 'Er—when was that, Dad?'

Her father thought about it. 'Oh, quite a while now. Couple of months. Before he went to Australia. He dropped in to say he'd be out of the country for a bit.'

Diana choked. 'How often have you been seeing him?'

It was Frank's turn to be surprised. 'Every month or so, I suppose. Didn't he mention it?'

Diana could have screamed. Instead she drew several long breaths and said in a careful voice, 'We've parted, Dad. We don't see each other.'

'But you've just been on holiday together,' he pointed out.

'Not,' she said between her teeth, 'voluntarily. If I'd known he was going to be there, wild horses wouldn't have got me to that damned castle.'

He looked worried. 'Oh, dear. I had no idea.' He bent down, peering into her face. 'But I thought... I mean your mother said... Aren't you getting back together again, then?'

Very slowly her hands closed into fists. She could feel the nails digging into her palms. But she said calmly, 'No, Dad. Not the last time I looked.'

He shook his head. 'I'm sorry,' he said simply. 'You're never going to be happy without him, you know.'

She winced. It was too horribly close to what she felt herself.

'Nor happy with him,' she said quietly.

He smiled at her affectionately. 'You're just going through a bad time,' he said. 'Marriage is a difficult relationship. But when Miles put that ring on your finger he meant it to stay there.'

She took it off that night when she got back. She thrust the ring deep into her handkerchief drawer, not looking where it fell. She should, she knew, have taken it off years ago. If she had really wanted to be free, she would have done.

'Heaven help me,' she muttered.

She began to work. It was late and she was tired but she knew if she went to bed she wouldn't sleep any more than she had slept last night. And the night before that, her hurt heart reminded her, she had slept dreamlessly deep in Miles's arms. Until he had left her.

She was at her desk, poring over a sketch plan by the light of an angled lamp, when the doorbell rang. She jumped, looking at the clock. After nine. Joan Dryden making house calls?

She picked up the entryphone. 'Hello?'

'And where the hell have you been?'

Even through the distorting device she could hear the menace in his voice. She clenched her hand round the instrument until her knuckles showed white.

'Who is that?' she demanded in as cool a voice as she could manage.

'Don't play games with me,' he advised softly. 'Let me in, or I'll raise the neighbourhood.'

He would too. It was a small residential square, with the house fronts facing inwards over a pedestrian path and the central shrubbery. It would be all too easy for him to bring the residents of all twelve houses out into the communal garden. He would probably, thought Diana in helpless anger, enjoy it.

She punched the entry button with quite unnecessary viciousness. At least she wasn't going to go down to the ground floor and let him in.

He came up the stairs two at a time. She listened for his steps as she had listened for them so many times before in the house they had shared.

I am not going to be sentimental, she vowed. And I'm not going to let him persuade me or browbeat me or seduce me. Particularly not seduce me.

She switched on the wall-lights as he got to the top of the stairs. He stood there looking round the open-plan sitting-room, pushing his hands through his hair.

'Sitting in the dark?' he mocked with a nod to the light-switch where her hand still lingered. 'Moping?'

Diana glared at him. 'Working,' she said coldly, indicating the desk and its workmanlike lighting arrangements. 'I didn't realise how late it had got.'

He gave a brisk nod. 'Then you won't have eaten. Get your coat.'

She stared at him. 'I'm sorry?' she said in a voice of ice.

'So you should be. Get your coat.'

She wasn't going to allow him to browbeat her, Diana reminded herself.

'I won't,' she said.

Miles gave her his most charming smile. He was looking at his most implacable.

'Then come as you are and freeze.'

'I'm not going anywhere with you.'

'Yes, you are,' he said positively. 'You're coming to have dinner. And then you're coming home with me.'

Diana retreated behind a sofa. 'This is my home.'

'You would be there now if I hadn't missed you at the airport,' he said, ignoring her.

Diana suddenly felt a surge of kindness for the small jumping bean who had sat next to her on the horrible flight. At least his company seemed to have camouflaged her arrival. If she had known Miles was in the crowd waiting for her she would have been frantic.

'You delude yourself, Miles,' she said. 'I would never have gone back to your house in any circumstances.'

His eyes narrowed. 'That isn't what your body was telling me two nights ago,' he said softly.

Diana flinched. So she'd found something else that hurt more than anything had ever done before or could do again, she thought with a touch of hysteria. How many more such records was she going to have to break before Miles got out of her life forever?

She said, 'I'd rather we didn't talk about that.'

'I'm sure you would.' He was grimly amused. 'We're going to talk about it, nevertheless.'

She might be determined not to be browbeaten but she knew her limitations, Diana thought. She made a despairing gesture.

'All right. Have your say. And then go away.'

'Only if you come with me.'

She closed her eyes. 'For the last time, Miles. *No.*'

'The night before last . . .'

She opened her eyes and glared at him. 'The night before last I behaved like a fool and a tramp.'

He might just as well not have been listening to her. He stretched out a hand and cupped her cheek as if they were lovers about to fall into each other's arms. His eyes were warm.

Damn him, thought Diana, suddenly sharply afraid of herself. She stepped back, wrenching her head aside.

'I've started divorce proceedings,' she said harshly.

That at least managed to get his attention, she saw with satisfaction.

'You've *what*?'

Prudently she didn't repeat it. It was all she could do to stand her ground. His eyes weren't warm any more. They were flaming. She thought suddenly, I've never seen him lose control of himself like this before. He will hate losing control.

He didn't touch her. But she felt the blast of his anger like a water-cannon. If she hadn't been holding on to the back of the sofa she could almost have staggered under the force of it.

'Don't bully me, Miles,' she flared.

He looked her up and down measuringly. 'Two nights ago, you were going mad in my arms,' he said levelly.

It was an accusation. Diana's face flamed.

'I——'

'You told me you loved me,' he said relentlessly.

Heaven help her, she probably had. She'd felt the love all right, Diana thought with a stab of misery. With her guard down like that, she'd probably been stupid enough to tell him as well. She shook her head at the thought.

'I assure you, you did.'

She gathered up the tatters of her pride and met his eyes.

'Very possibly,' she said in an even tone. 'In the heat of the moment one says these things. I'm afraid I don't remember.' Her shrug was a masterpiece.

Their eyes locked. His darkened.

Then he said softly, 'I don't believe you.'

She shrugged again, looking away.

'You were never much of a liar, my dear Diana. Especially not in bed,' he drawled.

If he had meant to be cruel, he could not have hit her with more precision.

Her voice like ice, she said, 'It's called sex, Miles. Chemical attraction. Of which you and I have rather too much for our own comfort. It's pretty ephemeral. It doesn't replace liking and trust. And you can't build a marriage on it.'

He stared at her. The handsome face looked gaunt suddenly.

'I won't let you get away with that,' he said.

Quite suddenly Diana realised that she was at the end of her tether. If he didn't leave, and soon, she was going to break down and start begging him to stay. And then he'd leave, without a backward look, until the next time...

'I can't bear it,' she said. 'I've had all I'm going to take from you, Miles...'

It was the wrong tone to take, the wrong thing to say. He was too near, the mood was too taut, they were too alone in the quiet house. He stepped round the sofa, his expression black.

'Now there you're wrong,' he said quite gently. And took hold of her.

Diana would have said she knew all there was to know about the way she and Miles made love. She would have been wrong.

There was none of the gentleness they were used to. None of the slow savouring of the delights of the senses. They were both hurt and angry and, both in their particular way, driven to the limit.

Diana didn't know who astonished her most—Miles, no longer silent and immaculately controlled, or herself, as fierce in her demands of their bodies as he was. When they fell back, gasping, she felt as if she had run through fire—and not wholly escaped the burning.

Miles was breathing hard. He reached out a long arm for her, drawing her back against his body.

'Di.' His voice was slurred but the amusement was back. If it hadn't been she might not have reacted as she did. But she was not in any case to be laughed at, with her heart still pounding and the bruises beginning to appear.

She wrenched herself away from all that dangerous warmth and laughter. He was never going to hurt her again. Never.

'My point proved, I think,' she said coldly. 'Sex, Miles. And nothing else.'

CHAPTER NINE

THIS time it was Diana who left. She stumbled into some clothes and drove her car to Joan Dryden's. She was, she freely admitted, lucky that the windy streets were empty at that time of night.

Joan took one look at her and sent her to bed with a hot drink. The next day she even came back to the little house with her distressed client. But Miles had gone by then.

The sitting-room still looked like a battlefield. A chair was on its side and papers were everywhere. Joan's eyebrows went up to her hairline.

'I'll get a "no molestation" order,' she said practically.

But Diana said swiftly, 'No. Don't do that. He won't be back again.'

Joan looked at her narrowly. 'You're sure of that?'

Diana thought of the bleakness in his eyes when she had looked down at him with that parting shot.

'I'm sure.'

Joan shrugged. 'Well, you know your own business best,' she said doubtfully. 'I'll get on to his solicitor anyway. He's still using Hendon, I presume?'

'I suppose so.'

Diana must have sounded as depressed as she felt. Joan touched her arm.

'What you need is a bit of forward planning. Go and look at the order book and see whether you can pay the bills,' she said bracingly. 'That'll put a bit of ginger into life, especially if you can't. Take care of yourself.'

Diana saw her off, then went slowly back indoors. Take care of yourself, she thought wryly. Well, she'd been doing that, hadn't she? Since long before Miles left, too. Miles had never wanted to take care of her. He'd been too impatient, too—other than in those moments of devastating passion—remote. She'd broken her heart on that remoteness. All the passion had done was hide it.

She was, Diana assured herself, better off taking care of herself and not looking, hopelessly, for love that wasn't there. Passion was no substitute. All it did was disguise Miles's deep indifference, and her own need to protect herself from him.

She took Joan's advice and listed all the work she had accepted and all that had been offered while she was away. She gave the computer some parameters and told it to prioritise. It came out with a schedule that, even assuming minimum travel, was full for six months.

'At least I won't starve,' Diana said wryly.

She looked uneasily at the papers on the Princess's apartment. She didn't need Miles's work. On the other hand, it would look like running away if she didn't at least attempt a report of sorts. And Miles wasn't going to have the satisfaction of having got her on the run, she told herself.

She would send him a nominal bill which she would be quite glad if he never paid. And then the whole relationship would be behind her.

The report on the Princess's apartment was typed and printed off by midnight.

She stood up, stretching her arms above her head. The queer silence of the small hours made her feel very alone. She bit her lip. Not alone. Lonely. For Miles. Her very skin called out for his touch. She lowered her arms abruptly.

'This has got to stop,' she said aloud between her teeth. 'It's over. I am never going to see him again. I don't *want* to see him again. I've got to get on with my life on my own.'

For the next four weeks she made a valiant attempt to do just that. She worked fourteen hours a day, leaving the answering machine as a barrier between her and the outside world. Miles neither wrote nor tried to call her. She was, Diana said to herself, thankful.

She went to see her parents on brief, irregular visits. She had checked with the solicitor and they were right. The house was in their own name now. At least Miles wasn't going to hold that over her head.

She had a faint suspicion her parents were still seeing Miles, though. It crystallised one Saturday evening when, watching a science programme on television about a new discovery, her father said cheerfully, 'That's over my head. Miles will have to explain it to me.'

Diana sat bolt upright. 'Dad——'

But her mother interposed smoothly, 'There'll be stuff in the Sunday papers, I shouldn't wonder. We'll look.'

At once she got up and began to fuss about evening drinks and Diana felt the opportunity to challenge her slip away. It was frustrating. She would, she thought grimly, have it out with both of them in the morning.

But Constance Silk had a heavy programme for her in the morning. She had to plant out seedlings, gather flowers for the house, go to the farm for cream. Diana did it all with a grim efficiency that must have told her mother that she wasn't going to avoid interrogation. Constance stayed serene.

'Your father's papers?' she suggested, receiving the carton of cream with a word of thanks.

'All right, Mother,' Diana agreed. 'I'll go to the village shop for you. *Then* we'll talk.'

'Of course, darling,' Constance agreed with the calm of a woman who had the next diversionary tactic well planned.

Diana laughed in spite of herself. But her mother wasn't going to get out of it, she promised herself. But in the end it was not Constance who diverted attention from the subject.

Diana strolled back along the metalled road with the papers under her arm, enjoying the scents of the June countryside. They were, she thought, utterly unlike the hot herbal smell of the Greek cliffs. They were heady and sweet—too sweet. And the road began to give off an odd sheen as if the tar was melting. The papers were very heavy. All of a sudden Diana realised she didn't feel very well.

She got home somehow. One look at her face and Constance Silk had her sitting on the doorstep with her head between her knees. Her father's wheelchair whirred agitatedly.

'No need to get in a flap, Frank,' Constance said calmly. 'She's got a touch of the sun, that's all.'

And, sure enough, she felt better after lunch. She drove home, forgetting the incident.

The following morning, however, was different. Diana awoke late and heavy-eyed with the feeling that something horrible was imminent. It was. She was sick.

It didn't last long. She recovered and went through the rest of her day as if it had not happened, though it was an effort. She had a strange feeling of exhaustion, which was infuriating with all the work she had to do. And when the same thing happened the next morning she lost patience with herself.

She hardly ever went to the doctor, so he was a stranger. He turned out to be young and horridly cheerful. He listened to her tale of the accident in Greece and the chance of slight concussion with an air of tolerant superiority which made Diana want to hit him.

'Well, we'll see what the tests say,' he conceded at last. 'But I'd say it was a slight touch of pregnancy, Mrs Tabard. Congratulations.'

Diana could never afterwards remember how she got herself out of his surgery and home. She must have driven but she had no memory of the journey. She felt cold. Panic, she knew. Panic and a strange, frightening sensation of being caught up in events over which she had no control.

For the moment the doctor had suggested it she had recognised it as the truth. She would wait for the test results, of course, but in her heart she already knew. She was carrying Miles's child.

'And what do I do *now*?' she asked her blank computer screen, feeling no less blank herself.

She thought about telling her parents, and shuddered. They would be overjoyed. They would also expect her to go back to Miles. She shuddered again, more deeply. She couldn't bear it. She *couldn't*.

There were occasions—short, ecstatic and unforeseeable moments—when he wanted her with a physical passion that, if you were very gullible, looked like love, Diana allowed. Felt like love, even. But then he would go away and not want her. He might want Susie Galatas, or some other worldly sophisticate who could match him, in those moods. But he wouldn't want Diana. And that would break her, she knew.

Diana tipped forward and leaned her hot forehead against the top of the computer screen. If you were very gullible or very much in love...she mused. If you were very much in love you saw what you wanted to see and only counted the cost afterwards. As she had counted the cost in the last two years.

'I can't do it again,' she said aloud. 'I wouldn't survive another blast.'

And yet. And yet . . .

Didn't Miles have a right to know that she was expecting his child? She knew if she were advising someone else she would disapprove violently of a woman not at least telling her child's father. Yet if she told him, what could she expect? Worse, what would she want?

Diana closed her eyes.

Face it, she told herself with fierce contempt, what you want is your fantasy back. Miles loving you. Miles wanting the baby. Miles holding your hand through all the things you're scared of: doctors and clinics and the whole bureaucracy. And getting ready for the baby. You don't want to do it alone. But it's more than that. You want Miles. Haven't you got any backbone at all? Haven't you learned *anything*?

The arguments went round and round, not just that day but all the days that followed. The results of the test came but Diana was not surprised at the result. She still didn't know what she was going to do. She put off going to see her parents that weekend. Constance's eyes were too sharp.

Every morning she woke up with the conviction that it would be all right if she told Miles. He was a civilised man and he would be considerate and helpful in a practical way. And then during the day she would lose her nerve. She would start to imagine herself taken over by him again, as he took charge of the situation. Or, worse, living with him, trying not to beg him to love her.

She could have found out where he was easily enough. If he was writing his paper for Moscow he was probably in Oxford anyway. Or Joan Dryden could have talked neutrally to his solicitor. Diana stayed silent.

She lost weight. Knowing it was bad for the baby, she began to watch her diet in a distracted way. She worked like a demon, and spent the small, sleepless hours knitting secret garments for a February baby. She knew that the time during which she could hope to keep her secret was running out.

And then Susie Galatas turned up, out of the blue, unannounced, standing on Diana's doorstep in glamorous scarlet with diamonds in her ears and round her slender wrist.

'Oh,' said Diana, conscious of bare feet and jeans and enormous hostility.

Susie's eyes gleamed for a moment, then were swiftly veiled.

'Busy?' she asked, following Diana into the sitting-room.

Diana took the excuse gratefully.

'I'm afraid so. So I don't want to be rude, Susie, but it's a quick coffee and goodbye, I'm afraid,' she told her uninvited guest.

Susie sat down in Diana's Victorian chair and inspected her bracelet.

'I think you were so sensible not to go back to Miles,' she said. 'Chris thought you would.' It was not quite a question.

Diana felt her face freeze into a mask. 'Milk in your coffee?'

Susie crossed exquisite legs. 'Of course, living here in Oxford you'll have heard the gossip. About him and the wife of the man he was working with. Yes, milk and a little sugar, please.'

Diana stirred milk and several teaspoonsful of sugar into the brew with unnecessary viciousness.

'That's why they cancelled the lecture tour, you know. The boffin found out that his wife was having an affair

with Miles and had a breakdown.' She took the coffee
and sipped. 'Personally, I always thought that was why
Miles wanted you to go back to him—to knock the rumours on the head. Though why he bothered...' She
shrugged. 'I suppose he must have wanted to go on
working with the husband.' She put her head on one
side. 'What do you think?'

'I think you've got a poisonous tongue and a worse
mind,' Diana said.

It was a great release to say it. Susie looked astonished.

'Steve and Hilary Gilman are Miles's friends. That's
not the way he treats friends,' Diana continued quietly.

Under the perfect make-up, Susie flushed.

'You know him so well, I suppose?'

'Well enough to know he doesn't cheat friends.'

Susie gave a trill of laughter that sounded forced. 'Oh,
they'll have hushed it up. The husband's gone into some
academic nut-house,' she said cruelly, 'and the devoted
wife's gone home to hold his hand. So Miles went to the
castle to play peasant and look for some longer-term
cover before he went back on the academic circuit: you.'

Diana looked at her with dislike.

'If it were true—which it isn't because Miles doesn't
do things like that—he wouldn't need cover,' she said in
a light, hard voice. 'Academics run off with other academics' wives all the time. It's a licensed university sport.'

Susie was pitying, and her tone was triumphant.

'Miles doesn't do things like run off with people,' she
said. 'I agree. He travels light. He doesn't want a lady
cluttering up his life. He's not into permanence.'

Unwarily, Diana shut her eyes. 'He was into permanence once.' She wasn't talking to Susie.

Susie made an angry noise. '*Darling*. How blind can
you be? Miles didn't marry in thirty-six years. He'd had
hundreds of women after him. Some of them were dev-

astating. He didn't marry because he didn't need to. When he saw you—well, frankly, darling, none of us could understand it. Until Chris said it had to be the only way he could get you. Then it made sense.' She pulled out a packet of cigarettes and lit one with unsteady fingers. 'That was how it was, wasn't it?'

Diana whitened.

There had been a night—nights—when Miles had taken her back to her graduate house and sat drinking coffee with her until the small hours. He had wanted more, urged her, demonstrated beyond any doubt that she wanted more as well. It had all been so new, so strong. She had hesitated.

Ironically, she had said to Miles that all that there was between them was sex. And here was Susie telling her the same thing.

'That's all,' said Susie, her eyes like diamonds. She drew rapidly on the cigarette. 'If you'd gone to bed with him, you'd have got rid of him inside three months like the rest of us.' She sounded furious.

Diana drew a careful breath. Susie was jealous, she told herself. Jealous and angry, though heaven knew why. Miles seemed to be more committed to her than he had ever been to his wife. But she knew the expression on Susie's face. The Countess was hurt and she wanted to lash out at someone. Diana could even sympathise with it, reluctantly.

She said gently, 'That's all in the past, Susie. There's no point in raking it over again. Now, was this only a social call or did you want me to do something for you?'

'The Princess's room,' said Susie, 'the man you told us to go to. The Italian? He says we need to have the paint made up specially if it's to be authentic. In England. *He* recommended *you*.'

Diana closed her eyes. That was undoubtedly Francesco trying to do her a good turn professionally after she recommended him to Castle Galatas. She cursed all friends.

'I'm really terribly busy. I couldn't fit you in for ages...'

Susie said swiftly, 'A weekend. That's all it would take. The Italian said so. You take photographs and scrapings of the existing paint and then come back and commission some firm you know here. They can ship the paint out to us without your ever going near them again. It needn't take long. Dimitri could fly you out.'

It was true. Diana glared at her.

Susie said stiffly, 'Miles told me to get it finished. He doesn't think I've got the sticking power. I—need help.'

It was that unvarnished statement that persuaded Diana. It couldn't be easy for the Countess to ask for help from someone she'd always despised. And Diana had some fellow feeling for her. Miles was an impossible taskmaster.

'All right,' she found herself saying. 'One weekend.' She put a hand over her stomach in an instinctive protective movement that Susie didn't notice. 'But soon.'

As Susie promised, Dimitri flew Diana out to Greece. He piloted the plane himself with another man whom he introduced as his navigator. He was friendly enough but businesslike. A laughing, holidaying Dimitri was, Diana realised, a different proposition from the serious man of affairs.

They landed at a small, private airstrip. The Galatas Mercedes was there to meet them. Dimitri handed her into it, bade goodbye to the navigator and got in beside her. He looked tired and preoccupied.

Diana said, 'Do you often spend weekends here?'

He shrugged, looking out of the window at the passing landscape. It was a uniform golden brown now; the green of spring had disappeared. It was very hot, too.

'I used to,' he said evenly. 'Lord knows why I've come this time. I don't know what game Susie's playing.'

He turned and Diana could see the pain in his eyes. It was a pain she was not a stranger to. She had an impulse to touch his hand, and curbed it. He wouldn't want pity any more than she did herself.

'I want her to marry me, you know.'

She nodded. 'Yes. I thought you did. I'm sorry.'

'I nearly asked her in the spring. She seemed as if she was changing, calming down a bit. Not chasing round all over the world the way she has been. This last winter I thought, At last. But——' He shrugged. 'Miles came back and she ran to him, just as she always does. As if they're still *children*.'

Diana's heart lurched. 'I'm sorry,' she said with difficulty. 'But I don't think he thinks of her as a child.'

He gave a brief laugh. 'He does,' he contradicted her. 'Because that's what she is. She refuses to grow up.'

Diana thought of the intensity she had sometimes detected in Susie Galatas. With sudden insight, she said positively, 'It won't be enough for her. She wants a husband. Children. I'm certain.'

This time his laugh was gentler. But he shook his head. 'She lives in a fantasy world,' he said.

There was only Maria to meet them when the car swept into the courtyard. Maria looked worried and was uncommunicative in the extreme. Diana was surprised, then decided that Maria must be embarrassed by what she could not help knowing about the circumstances of her parting with Miles. Whatever the reason, Maria's eyes didn't quite meet hers. And even before the chauffeur had taken their cases out of the car the housekeeper disappeared back into the kitchen muttering about supper.

The chauffeur led the way into the eighteenth-century part of the house. Dimitri was puzzled.

'I always have the tower room under Chris,' he objected. 'So I can listen to the sea.'

The chauffeur was wooden. 'The Countess said you were to have the lilac room, overlooking the terrace.'

Dimitri made a face. 'Susie pointing out she'll do as she pleases in her own house,' he deduced. 'She can be so childish sometimes,' he muttered, though Diana wasn't sure whether she was intended to hear.

He shrugged, anyway, and went in. The chauffeur led Diana round the corner of the corridor. She found that she, at least, was in the same room as before. So Susie was only playing power games with her rejected suitor.

Diana unpacked her overnight case briskly. Her kit for taking paint samples was the largest thing in it, she thought wryly, shaking out her creaseless lace and muslin. She sat down in front of the flower-framed mirror and unpinned her hair. She was brushing it with smooth, rhythmic strokes when, to her consternation, the door from her bathroom opened. She dropped her brush with a clatter and jumped to her feet.

'Who...?' she gasped, thinking, Not Miles. Please don't let Susie have betrayed me to Miles after all.

But to her amazement it was Dimitri. His face was like thunder.

'Do you know what that woman has done?' he almost shouted.

Diana was astonished. 'Maria?'

'Maria!' he spat. 'Of course not. The witch of the castle. Susanna Eleni Penelope Galatas.'

Diana prepared to be soothing and sympathetic. 'No. What?'

He seized her by the hand. 'Come with me.'

He marched her through the bathroom to the bedroom on the other side. It was full of flowers too.

'The lilac room,' Dimitri said grimly. 'Susie clearly thinks you and I should console each other.'

Diana quailed before his ferocity. If he was right, Susie, she thought, had been very unwise.

She said feebly, 'There must be some mistake.'

'No mistake. Susie,' said Dimitri with barely repressed violence, 'has played her last game with me. I bet she isn't even here.'

Diana stared. 'What? But she asked me for the weekend.'

'And me. She has set us up, my dear Diana, for a romantic weekend *à deux*.'

Diana sat down suddenly on the side of the bed. Her head was whirling unpleasantly. 'I don't believe it.'

He flung away and punched the bellpush in the wall as if it were a personal enemy.

'All right. We'll take statements,' he said grimly.

And when Maria arrived, knocking cautiously, he flung open the door and almost dragged her into the room.

'Where's the Countess, Maria?' he asked her without preamble.

Maria looked unhappy. She sent Diana a faintly apologetic look and launched into a flood of Greek. Dimitri's face darkened even more, if that were possible. He turned back to Diana.

'Unavoidably detained. She rang Maria this morning. I,' he said, 'am going to talk to her. Now.'

He stalked out, banging the door behind him. Maria looked after him with consternation. Diana put an alarmed hand to her suddenly tremulous stomach.

'I'm going to be sick,' she said on a rising note.

And Maria, taking one look at her white face, had no trouble at all in leaping the language barrier.

She wasn't in fact sick. But Maria put her to bed as tenderly as if she had been. Dimitri, Diana thought muzzily, would have had to wait an unconscionable time for his dinner.

The next morning she was awakened early. There were alien noises, loud and angry, which brought her up on one elbow. Straining her ears, she thought she caught Miles's deep tones. It was, she thought wryly, a product of pathetic wish-fulfilment. Oh, lord, would she never get him out of her blood? The slightest confusion in the distance and she thought it was Miles calling her.

The noises got louder. Yet it was hardly day. Beyond the open french windows, the dawn was streaking the horizon. Diana pushed her hair back, bewildered. And then she heard her name being called indeed, but not by Miles.

The door to her room was flung back and Susie rushed in. She was dishevelled and breathless, her sunburst scarves flying.

Diana sat up, startled. Her modest broderie anglaise nightdress slipped off one shoulder.

'What is it?' she demanded.

'When you didn't get to the flat, we thought Dimitri must have had an accident. We checked but no one knew anything. It never occurred to us that he would have brought you straight here. We were frantic.'

Diana plucked the only word out all of this which made any sense.

'We?' she said with foreboding.

Susie ignored that. Her eyes slid sideways.

'Susie, what have you done?' Diana asked in dawning alarm.

But there was no need for an answer. The door to the bathroom was pushed open and Miles strolled in.

For a timeless moment there was absolute silence in the opulent bedroom. Across the flowers and the heavy furniture Miles met her eyes, his expression unmistakable. Diana took in the naked hunger in one appalled second. She hauled the strap of her nightdress back into place with fingers that shook.

A quick glance told her that Susie, wringing her hands, was oblivious of that instantaneous, blazing signal. Diana's mouth was dry. She swallowed.

Susie turned to Miles, palms outspread.

'They were here together all night,' she said. 'I was going to tell him I'd marry him. I thought he loved me...'

Miles didn't speak. Something flickered in Susie's eyes. She whirled, draperies flying. 'Where is he?' Her voice rose to screaming-pitch. 'Bitch! Traitor! Where is he?'

Diana got out of bed. If she ever told Miles the truth about her night here with Dimitri, she knew she couldn't do it in front of a hysterical Susie. She was shaking. But she took hold of her courage and her common sense and faced the fierce Countess.

Susie screamed. And went on screaming. The look she turned on Diana was pure hatred.

Miles stepped between them. He looked cool and about as approachable as the moon. Had she imagined that blazing look? Would he believe his cousin's melodrama? And would he care?

There was a sharp crack as his hand connected with Susie's cheek, but his voice was gentle. 'That's enough, Susanna,' he said firmly. 'You're leaping to conclusions again.'

Susie's hand went to her reddening cheek. She didn't look glamorous and sophisticated any more. She looked like the child Dimitri called her. She was crying in great gulping sobs, like a schoolgirl.

'He—he...'

'You don't know what's happened yet,' Miles said, still in that steady voice.

But Susie was looking at Diana now and her expression was murderous.

'Oh, yes, I do,' she said fiercely, and made a dart at Diana.

Not expecting it, Diana flinched away and stumbled, cracking herself against the side of the bed. She gave an exclamation of pain at exactly the same time as Miles said in quite a different voice, '*Enough*!'

CHAPTER TEN

DIANA flinched at the iciness of it. If Miles had spoken to her like that, she thought, she would have turned and fled. Susie, though she stopped screaming, showed no such inclination.

She stared at him for a moment, her dark eyes huge.

'Oh, *Miles*,' she said heart-rendingly. And flung herself into his arms.

Diana flinched again, as his arms closed round the vibrant figure. She caught sight of the little tableau in the mirror behind them. They looked like three other people, actors on a screen, she thought. If she had been white before, she was now as pale as milk.

Susie was weeping over his shirt-front, heedless of her eye make-up. She seemed genuinely distraught.

'They were *here*, Miles. All night. Together.'

Miles was impassive. He detached Susie's clinging hands without visible emotion, propelling her into a chair. Susie's weeping redoubled. She clutched at him but, though he didn't slap her again, he ignored her. He turned decisively to Diana.

'Well?'

There was no blaze of desire in his face now. He was utterly controlled. Diana made a helpless gesture. She looked at the cold, handsome face and could not believe that they had ever been close, that he had ever lost control in her arms.

Her throat clogged. She couldn't speak. She shook her head.

Behind Miles, Susie said, 'You see, she can't deny it.' She sounded both wretched and triumphant.

Diana said, 'Miles please——' It was not much more than a whisper.

He did not take those cool eyes off her.

'Diana tells the truth.' It was very quiet, his dangerous quietness. He spoke over his shoulder to Susie, but it was Diana he was looking at. 'Even when it isn't what you want to hear. Only the truth.'

It was not, she thought, looking at the handsome, indifferent face, a compliment. Yes, she must have been mistaken earlier. He looked like a man who would never desire her again.

'They're *lovers*,' said Susie. 'She and Dimitri.' It was an accusation.

Miles looked at Diana levelly. 'Is that true?'

Her throat hurt. She shook her head. 'No,' she managed in a rasping voice she didn't recognise as her own.

The brown eyes stayed cool. He didn't say anything. All he did was give a little nod, as if that was what he expected. It didn't seem as if he cared at all. Susie gave a shriek.

'You don't believe her. You can't,' she cried.

She sounded like a child. Miles turned to look down at her. He looked like a judge, calm and determined.

'Susie, I've known you a long time but I know Diana better.' He sounded tired. 'I know the sort of woman she is.' His voice gentled. 'There's no doubt, my dear. If Diana says she and Dimitri didn't sleep together, then they didn't.'

Diana froze in astonishment. She held her breath as he turned Susie's mascara-streaked face up to him.

'My dear,' he said again, very gently, 'this has got to stop. You're not fourteen any more. And I can't rescue you from every situation you can't handle.'

Susie stared at him.

'I have my own life to lead, you know. And I'm afraid you're beginning to make that difficult.' His voice was kind but quite implacable. 'My own wife thinks I'm having an affair with you, Susie. I'm very sorry, my pet, but this nonsense has got to stop.'

Susie looked shattered. 'But she hates you, Miles,' she said, in a panting voice. She seemed on the verge of hysteria. 'She wouldn't have come to the castle if I hadn't sworn that you wouldn't be here and I didn't know where to get in touch with you.'

Miles looked like stone. His lips barely moved as he said, 'I know.'

'Oh, lord,' said Diana, unheeded.

His eyes flicked up and down her briefly. She could not discern any expression on his face at all. Then he turned back to Susie.

'That's still our business, Susie. Not yours. Just as your problems with Dimitri aren't my responsibility.'

Susie looked stricken. He had clearly shocked her. What he said must have registered for once, Diana thought, suddenly sorry for her.

'I never...' Susie began.

'Oh, but you did,' he corrected. His voice was gentle. But weary. 'Every love-affair, every failed job, every slight, every missed plane and unbooked hotel room—they've all been my responsibility to sort out, haven't they? And if I didn't come at once, then you went crazy.'

Susie stared at him, silenced, her mouth working furiously. She no longer looked remotely attractive. Diana couldn't bear it.

'Why?' she said, stepping forward impetuously. She was shivering. 'If you loved Dimitri, why on earth didn't you tell him? He wanted to marry you, for heaven's sake. Why keep dragging Miles into it?'

For the first time since he had slapped her, Susie's eyes left Miles. She turned to Diana, her mouth twitching. She looked distraught. But she looked fierce as well.

'Because he's *mine*,' Susie ground out. 'There were years when he didn't belong to anyone but me.'

'You're wrong,' Miles told her evenly. 'I don't belong to anyone. I never have and I never will.'

Diana's head went back as if she'd been hit. Susie saw it and laughed. There was something hectic in her laughter. She seemed to have lost all sense of normal restraint.

'Did you think he was yours, then? He wasn't. Never for a minute. You're so pleased with yourself because he says you tell the truth, aren't you? You think you're going to get him back. But you're not.'

Diana thought, This can't be happening. People don't *say* things like that, even if they think them. And with a sudden huge compassion, She's going to feel appalled when she realises what she's done.

But for the moment Susie was on a high. The spite and envy were wincingly obvious.

'He never trusted you. Never. He knew you thought he was old and boring. He knew you went out with his students, dancing with them, spending the night with them while he was working.'

She came close up to Diana and hissed into her face, 'He knew because I told him.'

Diana felt the world begin to sway again. She closed her eyes.

'That wasn't true,' she said quietly, opening them again.

The horrible streaked mask of a face grinned at her.

'I told him I'd seen you,' Susie said in triumph.

The look of venom was horrifying. Diana's heart lurched. She put a hand to her throat.

'Seen me?'

'The green dress at Lalande's. Solange showed it to me and said you'd bought it. It was one of a kind, of course. I knew that. I knew Miles would too. I told him I'd seen a girl who looked like you and wearing a green cobweb Lalande coming out of Simon Herriot's flat at five in the morning. One of the nights he didn't come home, of course. You even told me when they were. I pretended that I didn't think it could be you. I said I didn't think you'd ever been to Lalande. I said I was *sure* you couldn't afford one.'

And I, thought Diana, was so delighted with myself for wearing it on the night of the college ball. A surprise for Miles, who liked me to dress up. Out of character for me but a peace-offering to him, for a night that was intended to be a reconciliation. Reconciliation? Oh, lord! How he must have mistrusted me. She remembered the look on his face.

'You were very clever, Susie,' she acknowledged. Her heart hurt. She put a hand to her side. Her pulses were fluttering wildly. 'I played right into your hands, didn't I?'

Miles moved suddenly. He said, 'Understandably.' His voice was harsh. 'Tell me, Susie, did it ever occur to you that there might be occasions on which you weren't entitled to have your own way? Ever?'

Susie turned to look at him. 'You don't understand...'

He took a step forward. He looked, Diana thought with a sudden thrill of alarm, almost murderous.

'Oh, but I do,' he said, too gently. 'You have no scruples at all, do you? I knew you were clever and spoiled and didn't have enough to do with your time, but, God help me, I never dreamed of anything like this.'

'You shouldn't have married her,' Susie said obstinately. 'She didn't fit in.'

His eyes narrowed. 'And you told her so, I suppose?'

Susie gave him a smile that was pure malice.

'I didn't have to.'

Miles went white. Susie's eyes flickered. Watching, Diana saw her begin to realise what she had done. She backed away from him.

'She's not stupid. She could see it for herself,' she gabbled. 'It was obvious. She could never give you what you wanted. What you were used to.'

'What I wanted?' he repeated in that mild voice that sent ice down Diana's spine. 'And you told her that was you, I suppose?'

Susie quailed. 'Not—not exactly.'

'What, then?'

Susie's head came up. 'I didn't tell her anything,' she said softly. 'She could *see*.'

He took a stride forward. 'There was nothing to see—unless you told her some fairy-story to dress it up.'

Susie gave a harsh laugh. The sudden sound was almost shocking. Diana's sense of unreality increased.

'Don't be a fool, Miles,' Susie said contemptuously. 'She saw what any woman would have seen. You didn't go near her for days, but when I said I needed you, you rushed to my side. You don't have to be a genius to work out where your priorities lay.'

He said quite gently, 'Not my priorities. My desire to minimise your nuisance value.'

Susie winced. There was a perfectly horrible silence. Diana's head began to swim.

'You know,' Miles said musingly, 'until I met Diana I thought most women were like that. Attention-seeking,' he explained with a cruelty that was all the worse for the considered, judicial tone in which it was uttered. 'Self-willed. Trivial. Making trouble and requiring other people to sort it out. Basically a nuisance if a man let them get too close. Where I went wrong,' he concluded thoughtfully, 'was in not realising you were a dangerous nuisance. You really don't have any glimmering of a conscience about all this, do you, Susie?'

Susie stared at him for an uncomprehending moment. Her eyes blinked convulsively. Then, all of a sudden, she whirled on Diana.

'You!' she was shouting. 'It's all your fault. You've turned him against me...'

Diana had a snatched vision of a harridan's face with flying hair and vengefully reaching hands. She cried out just as there was a wild shriek and Miles caught Susie. He lifted her off her feet and away from Diana.

But it was too much for Diana's uncertain hold on consciousness. Her blood began to thump until it was a pain in her head. She put out an uncertain hand. She thought she heard Miles cursing, fluently and at length. She wasn't sure why or whether it was her fault again. But she felt too faint to care.

She put out a hand to the chair-back. Missed. And toppled sideways on to the rug.

When she returned to her senses the sun was shining brilliantly through her open window. She lay for a moment, bemused. The wafting curtains and the elaborate furniture did not belong to the simple bedroom she had inhabited since she and Miles parted. Then she caught the scent of jasmine and everything came back with a rush.

'Oh, good grief,' she said aloud, sitting up abruptly.

'You're awake,' a voice said with satisfaction.

She knew the smooth tones. Her heart clenched. She turned her head. Miles was sitting on the chaise-longue with his long legs stretched out in front of him. The cushions at his shoulder were flattened. He looked as if he'd been there some time.

The white anger that he had shown Susie had gone. He looked tired but his face was no longer pinched and burning. She gave a shuddering sigh of relief.

He stood up and strolled over to the bed.

'Better?' he asked.

Diana met his eyes and found a message in them that brought the blood surging into her cheeks.

'Er—yes,' she said distractedly. 'Thank you.'

He touched the back of his hand briefly to her cheek. 'Good.'

Did he sound amused? Diana was confused. Surely he had been angry—cold and angry, just as he had been on the night he left, as if he couldn't bear to see her... Her thoughts stopped abruptly as she remembered everything that Susie had let fall. For no reason that she could think of she flushed again.

'Well enough to talk?' he asked lightly.

'About what?' she asked, wary.

'Us. Don't you think it's time?'

Her eyes fell. Was this where he agreed to a divorce? It was what she wanted of course, she told herself. Her heart plunged at the thought.

She said past the constriction in her throat, 'Not here. Not now, this minute. Let me get up and collect myself.'

There was a little silence. 'Time to get the armour back on, Diana?' he asked, an edge to his voice.

She didn't look at him. 'A few clothes, anyway.'

He gave a short bark of laughter. 'Well, that makes sense, I suppose.'

Diana didn't pretend to misunderstand him. She lifted her eyes. 'If we're going to talk sensibly, you have to promise to...to...'

'To keep my hands off you,' Miles supplied coolly.

Diana stiffened. She refused to blush a third time.

'Well, you haven't been very good at that in the immediate past, have you?' she reminded him.

And I have the consequences to prove it, she added silently.

Miles's eyes narrowed. But all he said was, 'Granted. OK—a nice neutral discussion in full armour with a ton of garden furniture between us. That make you feel safe? Or do you want a chaperon?'

Nothing would make her feel safe with Miles. Her own heart betrayed her over and over again, she thought wryly.

But she said with composure, 'That won't be necessary. Thank you.'

'I'll get Maria to make up a breakfast tray. I'll be out on the terrace when you're ready.' He nodded to the open window.

'Very well.'

Their eyes locked. Diana clenched her fingers over the coverlet. She lifted her chin defiantly. He looked at her taut fingers. His mouth twisted. Then he shrugged imperceptibly, turned and walked out on to the terrace.

As soon as the curtains billowed behind him, Diana darted out of bed, seizing a handful of clothes at random from her suitcase, and bolted into the bathroom.

She took a long time over her bath. The early morning nausea to which she had become accustomed passed as she dallied in the lilac-scented water. She sank her shoulders under the warm water, relaxing her muscles deliberately. If she was going to negotiate with Miles, she would have to be as calm as she could manage. Calm, controlled and unemotional.

Diana laughed bitterly. Was she ever going to feel unemotional in the same room as Miles?

Anyway, she had to try. She put on a cool cotton blouse and workmanlike jeans. She brushed her hair till it shone and pinned it on the top of her head. Peering at her image in the mirror, she wasn't pleased with her pallor. She didn't look as well as she had when she left Greece, and there was no way to disguise it.

Was it possible that Miles would be able to detect her pregnancy? Might he even suspect it already? And, whether he suspected or not, what ought she to tell him, now that they were to talk about their future?

Diana bit her lip. She didn't know. And there was no disguising that either. She shook her head, sighing. She hadn't been particularly clear-headed on the issue in the first place. Seeing Miles had only thrown her into greater turmoil.

Straightening her shoulders, she went out to him. The lemon grove in the distance looked golden yellow under the early morning sun, with the grey-green olives and nearly black cypresses behind them. It looked like a magic grove, Diana thought. The contrast between the beauty and the tense interview before her was all too sharp. She set her teeth.

Miles stood up as soon as he saw her. He had been sitting at the white ironwork table, frowning into the middle distance. A tray containing bowls of yoghurt and honey, sweet rolls and a steaming coffee-pot stood in front of him. His expression, Diana registered, was carefully neutral.

'Breakfast,' he said, indicating the tray. 'Maria's most anxious that you keep your strength up.'

In spite of her determined cool, Diana jumped. She didn't want to examine the possible implications of Maria's concern. She saw his eyes narrow again and said quickly, 'That's kind of her. I got the impression that she didn't approve of me yesterday. She wasn't terribly welcoming.'

'She thought you were here on a dirty weekend with Dimitri,' he said coolly. 'She didn't approve.'

Diana gaped. 'Why...?'

His eyebrows rose. 'Because you're my wife,' he said. 'She's old-fashioned like that.'

Diana said hurriedly, 'I didn't mean that. I meant why did she think it.'

He shrugged. 'It looked a bit like that, you have to admit. People don't believe in those sort of coincidences. Susie thought the same.'

Diana swallowed. 'You didn't,' she remembered.

His eyes were very steady. 'No,' he agreed quietly. 'I didn't.'

Diana decided she didn't want to examine the implications of that either. She sat down. She chose the chair furthest from his own. She watched him register it and the thin mouth slant at her choice. She reached for coffee.

'Susie—er—rather sees things from her own perspective, I think,' she said with constraint.

Miles sat down too. 'Black,' he said absently. 'Doesn't she just, though? And then spreads it around. It's amazing that people still believe her.'

Diana said gently, 'She believes herself. That's what makes it convincing.'

'I suppose so.' He sent her a long look. 'She did quite a number on us,' he said carefully.

Diana didn't answer immediately. She poured two cups of coffee and gave him his. She swirled milk into her own and stirred it, concentrating. She said slowly, 'If things had been right between us, Susie couldn't have done a thing.'

His face was mask-like. He didn't touch his coffee. She could feel his eyes on her, even though she wasn't looking at him.

'So what was wrong?' he said softly at last.

Diana tensed. She stirred the spoon round the boat-shaped coffee-cup as if her life depended on it. The sun was beginning to warm the back of her neck. It was going to be a blistering day, she thought irrelevantly.

'Don't you know?' she muttered.

He lifted his shoulders. 'I have my theories,' he said in his most cynical voice. 'I'd be interested in yours.'

Diana winced. 'I'd say we were incompatible from the start,' she told him. Her heart felt scorched by the lie. But she couldn't afford to give him any weapons. Least of all her unsuppressed love. 'It was just wrong.'

He didn't answer at once. Instead, he stretched his long legs out in front of him and turned his face up to the sun.

'I wouldn't say that,' he drawled at last. 'In fact in the early stages I'd say it was just about as right as it could be.' He flashed her an amused, under-browed look. 'Or don't you remember?'

Diana put her spoon down very deliberately. 'I remember.' She still wouldn't look at him.

'A marriage of true minds,' he said softly. 'To say nothing of hearts. Or bodies.'

He reached out and took her wrist in a light clasp. Diana jumped, her eyes flying at last to his face. But she didn't pull away. Under his fingertips, her blood was racing.

'I wasn't talking about sex,' Diana said in a stifled voice.

His thumb moved gently, soothingly over the frail wrist.

'Neither was I,' he insisted.

He sounded amused again. Diana tore her wrist away.

'Don't *do* that,' she said raggedly.

'Why not?'

She rounded on him suddenly, her eyes meeting his in desperation.

'It's just a game to you, isn't it?' she cried.

Miles looked blank. 'What?'

'Susie's a nuisance. So were your other ex-girlfriends. I, on the other hand, know my place better and keep out of the way when I'm not wanted.' She was bitter. 'Do you think I find that flattering?'

He sat up very straight. 'I wasn't intending to flatter you, no.' He still sounded unforgivably amused.

Diana pounded her hands on the arms of the chair. 'You don't *care* about any of us, do you?' His eyebrows flew up. 'You manipulate me. All of us. You're no better than Susie,' she flung at him. 'You just decide what you want and then move people around like chess-pieces until you get it.'

There was a pause. He did not, she noticed, try to deny the accusation.

Then he said levelly, 'If that were true, I haven't been very successful with you, have I?'

No word of affection, she noted. This was awful. Diana shut her eyes. She remembered Susie's allegations about his partner's wife. All of a sudden they didn't sound so unlikely.

'When she told me you wanted me back for camouflage, I didn't believe her,' she said almost to herself. She shook her head. The pain was almost physical.

Miles said impatiently, 'What on earth are you talking about?'

'Did you think I wouldn't hear about it?' She opened her eyes. She was trembling with what she assured herself was temper. 'Steve's ill, isn't he? That's why you had to cut the tour short. And Hilary's the problem, isn't she?'

He stared at her for a long moment as if she were speaking in a foreign language.

'Hilary?'

'Oh, don't try to pretend,' Diana said in a fury. 'I know what you want, Miles. Steve got suspicious, didn't he? And you need Steve's work. So you had to convince him.'

Something flickered in Miles's eyes. 'Hilary Gilman's the problem,' he said on a slow note of discovery. He almost sounded as if he was laughing again.

Diana felt as if he'd hit her. She swung round with her back to him.

'At least you admit it,' she said in a suffocated voice.

'I admit nothing,' Miles drawled. 'It was you who said Hilary was the problem; not me. The only problem I've had with Hilary is when she flung it in my face that I was halfway human when I was married to you and the sooner I got you back, the better for all my colleagues.'

'*What*?'

He put his hands on her shoulders and turned her gently round to face him.

'Listen, my—— Listen, Diana. Hilary Gilman's a friend.' He paused. 'Or she was. At the moment she blames me for Steve's illness.'

Diana said fearfully, 'Irreversible breakdown?'

'Good lord, no.' Miles stared down at her. His hands fell away from her shoulders. 'Where did you get that idea? He picked up a virus. It was bad enough, heaven knows. He was pretty well exhausted already. When he couldn't shake off the virus he got badly depressed. That's why we cancelled the tour. Depressed about his *work*,' he said gently. 'Nothing to do with an imaginary fancy I had for his wife.' He added reflectively, 'Hilary said it was my fault because I'd been driving us both so hard. I do that when I'm trying to forget.'

'But Susie said——'

'Susie!' His eyes narrowed. 'All right, tell me. How did Susie dress it up for you? I'd driven Steve to paranoia and was consoling Hilary?'

Diana shook her head. 'She said you'd been having an affair. That when Steve found out he had a nervous breakdown. That that was why——' She broke off.

'Why?' he prompted.

Her eyes fell. 'Why you wanted me back.'

'Ah. That accounts for the crack about camouflage,' Miles said affably. 'I wondered. He shook her gently. 'I'm surprised at you, Diana. You ought to know me better than that.'

She scanned his face. There was something there she didn't understand. It wasn't unkind but it was unyielding—a sort of amused determination. She felt her heart flutter and pressed her hand instinctively to the place where their child lay.

He feathered his thumb across her lips. Diana gave a long sigh.

'Yes,' she agreed. 'Yes, I suppose I did. If you'd wanted Hilary, you wouldn't have tried to keep it a secret. No matter how much you needed Steve's professional co-operation.'

His eyes glinted. 'Well, thank you, ma'am,' he drawled. 'An endorsement of my integrity, if not my sexual morals.' He was teasing.

For some reason that made her blush. She said hurriedly, 'I didn't really think...I mean I told Susie you wouldn't do anything hole-and-corner, no matter what she said.'

'You know me better than she does,' he agreed. 'And if you weren't blinded by jealousy you'd know that I don't care a row of beans for Hilary Gilman either.'

Diana tore herself away from him. 'I—am—not—jealous.'

Miles did not attempt to hold on to her. He looked at her for a moment, taking in her ruffled breathing and over-bright eyes. Then he shrugged, very slightly, and sat down again, patting the chair beside him.

Diana ignored that. He smiled crookedly. He looked up at her, the brown eyes narrowed against the sun. He looked singularly unagitated, to add to her fury.

'Yes, you are.' He sounded pleased.

Diana glared at him. 'And you are the most arrogant, complacent, *unprincipled* man I've ever met.'

'Would you say I was unprincipled?' Miles asked mildly.

'I just did,' Diana pointed out. She took a couple of calming breaths and said more quietly, 'I know you think it's funny, Miles. But I'm fresh out of a sense of humour where you're concerned.'

He smiled up at her. 'Interesting.'

'It isn't interesting,' Diana contradicted him. She had a horrible suspicion she was all too close to tears. Where was the strong, self-determining character she had been so proud of becoming? 'It's a damned nuisance. And very discouraging,' she admitted on a sigh.

He shook his head. 'On the contrary. It's the most encouraging thing I've heard in a long time.'

Diana stared at him suspiciously. His smile slanted.

'It's a sign that you care,' he explained quietly.

She scanned his face. He wasn't laughing any more. He stood up again suddenly. Diana tensed. But he made no attempt to touch her.

'You do care, don't you?' He might have formed it like a question but it was a statement of fact and they both knew it.

Diana made a small, despairing gesture, turning away.

'Diana——'

She closed her eyes, screwing them up tight against the threatened tears.

'Don't make me admit it,' she begged. 'You've taken everything else. Leave me my pride.'

Miles said softly, 'Will your pride feel better if I tell you I love you? That I haven't had a day's happiness since we parted? That I'll do any damned thing you say to get you back?'

Diana whirled, suspecting him of some dark mockery. But the brown eyes were unguarded. His smile twisted.

'Don't look so incredulous. Everyone knows but you.'

She felt as if the cool terrace tiles were shifting beneath her feet.

'Everyone?' she echoed.

He stood very still. 'Chris. Your parents. My mother.'

Diana thought of her parents' bland refusal to acknowledge that their parting was permanent. Was it more than a determined attempt to ignore the hurtfulness of the parting? Did they really believe that Miles wanted his wife back? Did they have reasons to believe it? She remembered that she had suspected they had been seeing him. What had he said to them?

'And they know you well enough to know when you're telling the truth?' she asked, almost of herself.

He said harshly, 'What have I ever done to make you mistrust me so much?'

At least that was something she had an answer to.

'You left me,' she said with spirit. 'You froze me out for weeks before you went. How do I know what you were doing those evenings when you said you were in college? You could have been seeing Hilary Gilman or Susie or any one of a hundred other women even then. How do I know you weren't?'

'Because you know me,' Miles said. As if it was obvious.

That stopped her. 'Do I?'

'You know you do. Better than anyone.' His voice was gentle.

'But——' All her hesitations were in her eyes. 'The women you knew—they were all so much more polished than I was. Sophisticated.'

'And you thought I was attracted to sophisticated women?' He shook his head, his eyes alight with laughter—and something more. 'After all the trouble I took to get you in my net?'

'It seemed reasonable.' Diana was defensive.

'More reasonable than the self-evident fact that I'm crazy about you?' Miles demanded evenly.

Diana gasped. Somewhere inside she began to tremble uncontrollably. He mustn't see it.

'Not self-evident to me,' she managed.

'All right. Maybe I made the wrong moves when we were together. But here, in the castle—what did you think I was doing when I kept carrying you off and making love to you?' Miles said in exasperation.

Diana swallowed. 'I thought it was a calculated attempt to make me come back and pretend. So you had the freedom to do whatever you wanted. Including walk away from me when you had more important things to think about.'

He raised his eyebrows. 'Calculated?' he echoed. 'You must think highly of my powers of acting.'

Diana flushed. 'We respond to each other. We always have,' she muttered. 'That doesn't mean . . .'

'That I'm honest or that I care for you?' he suggested softly as she hesitated.

'Miles,' she said at last, hanging on to the rags of her composure with resolution, 'you've got to understand— when you left me, I was devastated. I knew something was going wrong but I didn't know what I'd done. I fell apart. When I managed to piece my life back together again, I promised myself that no one would ever be able to do that to me again. Just because you happened to be here . . .'

She stopped as Miles made a rude noise. 'I didn't happen to be here, my darling. It was very carefully planned,' he said deliberately.

She stared.

'The commission to do the Princess's room was my idea. Chris didn't want to get involved to begin with but I pushed him. I knew I needed to see you, and your solicitor wouldn't let me near you. Even your parents wouldn't give me your address and they wanted us to get together again. But they said it was up to you to decide when you wanted to see me. And you didn't. So— I took steps. All right, manipulation if you like, but I was desperate.'

He didn't look desperate, Diana thought. He looked cool and confident and utterly in control.

'I thought if I could get you here alone... But I reckoned without Susie.' His tone was rueful. 'With her usual impeccable timing, she announced she was coming here herself. She'd had another of her misunderstandings with Dimitri. The castle has always been her bolt-hole. In a way she has as much right here as I have, so I couldn't bar the door against her. I tried to talk her out of it but...' He shrugged. 'So I got Chris to bring Dimitri down as well and see if he could do a bit of discreet patching up.'

Diana said, 'But she virtually ignored him.'

'That's love for you, my darling,' Miles said lightly. '*You* virtually ignored *me*.' He eyed her hopefully.

She winced, refusing to rise to the bait.

'Why didn't you cancel my visit, then? If all your stage management was going wrong.'

His mouth quirked in self-mockery. 'I couldn't bear to wait another day. And anyway——' he looked down at her with that wicked challenge she recognised '—not all my stage management went wrong. I told Maria to make sure when you arrived that you were brought to me and only me.'

Diana knitted her brows, remembering. She stiffened.

'You mean it wasn't an accident, that first time when Maria showed me into your room?' she asked.

The brown eyes danced. 'Well, I wasn't supposed to be in bed. Or at least not asleep,' he temporised. 'You arrived earlier than I'd allowed for. I did tell you at the time,' he reminded her.

'*Oh!*' she exclaimed in outrage.

He seized her hands, cupping them in his own and stroking them.

'Nothing else was planned,' he said rapidly. 'When I saw you—I lost my head. You were so beautiful. And you looked more fragile than the last time I'd seen you. Fragile and hurt. I thought, I can't play games with this woman. It's too important.'

'I hated you,' Diana said under her breath.

'It showed.'

'Making me want you like that.'

His hands stilled. 'Did I?'

She swallowed hard, raised her chin and told him the truth. 'At once. Just by turning over and holding out your hand. I was so *ashamed.*'

Miles looked down at her, not saying anything. She could feel the beat of his blood in the hands holding her. Her mouth was wry. 'I'd got rid of all that, hadn't I? I was strong and independent and I didn't need anyone. And then all of a sudden there you were, proving it was all a sham. I was furious. And scared.'

He frowned quickly. 'Scared?'

'I thought, I need him. I probably can't live without him. And I can't have him.'

'Oh, my darling,' he said, pulling her into his arms.

He kissed her fiercely. After a longer time without oxygen than she would have believed possible, Miles raised his head.

'Calculated?' he asked, though there was a faint tremor below the amusement.

Diana put up a wondering hand and touched his face.

'No. I accept that was spontaneous——'

'Passion,' Miles supplied, 'is the word you're looking for.'

Diana gave a slow, sweet shiver. 'Passion can be deceptive.'

'Not between us,' he said positively. 'If we'd listened to our feelings instead of other people's neat, logical lies, we'd never have parted. Or fought as we have these last weeks.'

Diana smiled into his eyes. 'It didn't feel like fighting all the time,' she murmured.

His eyes were intent. 'No?'

'Just most of the time,' she amended mischievously.

His arms tightened painfully. 'Oh, lord, I remember. You seemed as if you wouldn't talk to me, or even look at me most of the time. And then—that day on the launch, when you said something about walking tight-ropes on boats, I thought, She is looking at me, after all. There's hope.'

Diana blushed. 'Well, you scared me.'

'And you scared me in those damned caves,' Miles said with feeling. 'I thought, What will I do if she's hurt?' His voice rasped.

She shivered again. 'I know. I felt the same when you dived. I thought you were going to kill yourself. And I knew if you did that was the end. Until then I hadn't realised I was still—hoping. That scared me too, in a different way. I was pretty horrid to you after that, wasn't I?'

'I forgive you.'

'And I listened to Susie's malice.'

'I forgive you that too,' Miles said, kissing her eyebrow thoughtfully. 'She's very convincing, as I know to my cost. She kept telling me I was too old for you. That I'd spoilt your life.'

Diana made a small sound of distress. 'Did it seem to you that you had?'

Miles's smile was crooked. 'Not at first, no. But you were such a gentle girl. You wouldn't have told me. And I was working like a demon. When I came home in the small hours sometimes you used to look at me as if I were a stranger.'

'Whenever I saw her, Susie kept hinting that I wasn't really sophisticated enough for you,' Diana said in a small voice. 'When you stayed away so much—it seemed as if she was right.'

He compressed his mouth. 'I kept expecting you to find someone else,' he said quietly.

Diana stared. At last she said slowly, 'But you said this morning you trusted me.'

'I do. In a way I always did. But I was never sure I'd been fair to you, gathering you up into marriage the way I did. You'd hardly had time to look round at other men. And I was nearly old enough to be your father.'

There was real pain beneath the light tone. This, she saw suddenly, was important. This was the heart of their misunderstandings. And it needed careful handling. Any hint of sentimentality—still worse, compassion—and she would lose his trust forever.

Diana held herself away from him, her eyes glinting. 'Not unless you were extraordinarily precocious,' she said.

He laughed then. 'You always said that. But Susie...'

'Susie,' Diana said thoughtfully, 'said you'd only married me because you couldn't get me any other way.'

A gleam came into Miles's eyes. She found his fingers were busy with the pins in her hair.

'Susie has a commonplace mind,' he said mischievously. 'There were lots of other ways I could get you.' He chuckled as her eyes flashed, and listed them. 'Kidnap. Blackmail. Torture. Tickets for the Venice Biennale. Or plain seduction.'

Her hair fell free over his hands. He fanned it out pleasurably.

She said with a little difficulty, 'But you never did. Not before we were married.'

He looked down at her. 'Because I wanted you to be sure,' he said simply. 'I knew the moment I saw you. But you—you had no experience, no knowledge of the world. It was a much bigger gamble for you than me. Then—when Susie dropped clues that you were seeing other men, men more your own age—well, it was no more than I was braced for already. Do you see?'

She felt humbled. She should have made him more sure of her love than that. She took his face between her hands.

'Yes. I see. And I felt young and naïve and out of my depth so I retreated behind my pride.'

'Pride's a killer,' he agreed, kissing her.

So this was where she had to ditch her pride, Diana realised. Miles had made all the declarations so far. If they were to go forward, this was where she had to take some risks of her own.

She said painfully, not looking at him, 'Why did you leave me? After we'd spent the night together here, I mean. I—it felt as if you'd abandoned me again.'

He looked horrified.

'Oh, lord, my darling, I never thought of that. All I could think of was getting Susie and her troubles out of my hair. I took her to Athens. I told her she and Dimitri had to sort out their problems on neutral territory. Then when I came back and you were gone—I couldn't believe it. Not after that night.'

She hadn't believed it either, that apparent betrayal—not after that night. She drew a deep breath. This needed all her courage.

She cleared her throat. 'Er—Miles?'

'Mmm?' He was looking at her with a warmth that she would never have believed possible. Her whole body went into a slow burn, under that look. She could feel the blush rising.

She shut her eyes. 'I love you very much and please will you make love to me?' she gabbled.

He stood very still, then his arms went round her, tightening painfully. He gave a low laugh, and hoisted her into his arms in a sudden movement that made her squeak with alarm.

'At once,' he said solemnly.

Rather later, when the cicadas had joined the sun and there were faint, distant sounds of activity in the courtyard, Diana raised her head from his smooth brown chest and said, 'Miles, where are we going to live?'

He smiled, curling her hair round his fingers.

'The Moon? The Garden of Dreams?'

She kissed his nose. 'I'm serious. Do you want to go back to the old house in Oxford?'

'Not necessarily. Not if it has bad memories for you,' he said quietly.

'It doesn't,' she assured him. 'Only...'

'Or I suppose an interior decorator wants something more stylish. A Finnish ranch with a sauna on the roof?' he suggested.

'You know perfectly well I'm not that sort of decorator. Though I'll need my own study this time,' she warned.

'Certainly,' said Miles, closing his eyes. 'Whichever room you want. I believe in female liberation. As long as you move your own things.'

Diana tickled his ribs. 'Not in my condition,' she said gleefully.

He sat bolt upright, tumbling her off his chest. She looked up at him innocently.

'Are you...?' He stopped and started again. 'Are you telling me...?'

'We'll need a nursery. The small room next to the top-floor bathroom, maybe. There's another manipulative Galatas on the way.'

He bent over her, kissing her as if he would never stop. Eventually she called a halt, breathless and laughing.

'You don't mind?' she asked, her last fear gone.

He was honestly amazed. 'Di, it's wonderful.' He paused suddenly. 'As long as you don't?'

She shook her head. 'I was scared when I first found out. I kept thinking that everything would be all right if only I had you to hold my hand. Now I've got you——' she kissed his shoulder '——everything will be all right. Just as long as you're with me.'

Miles tightened his embrace. 'Forever,' he told her seriously. 'Forever.'

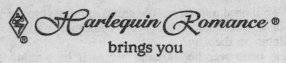

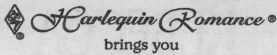

Harlequin Romance ®

brings you

HOLDING OUT FOR A HERO

Some men are worth waiting for!

Every month for a whole year Harlequin Romance
will be bringing you some of the world's most eligible
men in our special **Holding Out for a Hero**
miniseries. They're handsome, they're charming but,
best of all, they're single! Twelve lucky women are
about to discover that finding Mr. Right is not a
problem—it's holding on to him!

In September watch for:

> **#3425 *REBEL IN DISGUISE***
> **by Lucy Gordon**

Available wherever Harlequin books are sold.

Look us up on-line at: http://www.romance.net

HOFH-9

REBECCA

43 LIGHT STREET

YORK

FACE TO FACE

*Bestselling author Rebecca York returns to "43 Light Street"
for an original story of past secrets, deadly deceptions—and
the most intimate betrayal.*

She woke in a hospital—with amnesia…and with child.
According to her rescuer, whose striking face is the last
image she remembers, she's Justine Hollingsworth. But
nothing about her life seems to fit, except for the baby
inside her and Mike Lancer's arms around her. Consumed
by forbidden passion and racked by nameless fear, she
must discover if she is Justine…or the victim of some mind
game. Her life—and her unborn child's—depends on it….

Don't miss *Face To Face*—Available in October, wherever
Harlequin books are sold.

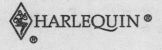

HARLEQUIN ®